HOMES FOR WILDLIFE

A PLANNING GUIDE FOR HABITAT ENHANCEMENT ON SCHOOL GROUNDS

Written and edited by Marilyn C. Wyzga

Illustrated by Victor E. Young

Developed by the New Hampshire Fish & Game Department

The Department receives federal funds. Under federal law, discrimination is prohibited on the basis of race, color, national origin, or handicap. If you think you have been discriminated against in any program, activity or facility or want more information, contact the New Hampshire Fish & Game Department or the Office of Equal Opportunity, U.S. Dept. of the Interior, Washington, DC 20240.

Technical Wildlife Consultants:
John Kanter, Wildlife Specialist, University of New Hampshire
Cooperative Extension
David Langley, Assistant Wildlife Specialist, University of New
Hampshire Cooperative Extension

Advisory Committee:
Ellie Horwitz, Massachusetts Division of Fisheries & Wildlife
Lisa Kane, Maine Department of Fish & Wildlife
Marion Larson, Massachusetts Division of Fisheries & Wildlife
Judy Silverberg, New Hampshire Department of Fish & Game

Technical School Sites Advisors:
Jerry Schierloh, New Jersey School of Conservation, Montclair
State College
Dennis Yockers, Ph.D, Wisconsin Department of Public Instruction

This project was made possible with funding from:
the United States Fish and Wildlife Service, Office of Extension
Publications, through the University of New Hampshire
Cooperative Extension,
the New Hampshire Chapter of the Wild Turkey Federation, and
the New Hampshire Fish & Game Department.

Cover photographs:
Scarlet Tanager, © 1998 Alan Briere
Children in Schoolyard, Marilyn Wyzga

Homes for Wildlife, © 1993, 1998 New Hampshire Fish and Game
Department, 2 Hazen Drive, Concord, NH 03301. All Rights Reserved

ISBN: 0-9652156-2-8

Printed on recycled paper

UNIVERSITY OF
NEW HAMPSHIRE
COOPERATIVE EXTENSION

Table of Contents

Preface

School grounds can be healthy habitats for people and wildlife, and unique learning labs. *Homes for Wildlife* can help make it happen. The process outlined in this guide provides students and teachers the opportunity for direct, hands-on learning in the environment of their schoolyards. As you design and carry out an enhancement plan, you become more informed about wildlife needs and ways you can effect positive change. In the process, you grow an outdoor classroom.

This guide outlines a process for assessing and mapping the schoolyard site, developing a plan, and implementing enhancement projects, with supplementary information to support the effort and make it a success. All information is geared towards grades K-8. Developmentally appropriate activities for each age group allow every student to contribute on their own level as they participate in team planning and activities.

Homes for Wildlife grew from the enthusiasm and interest of teachers using the Project WILD curriculum materials, to put the WILD concepts into practical action in the schoolyard. As you implement the process outlined in these pages, we'd like to hear from you. Your challenges and successes can serve as a model for others in this rapidly expanding network of schools landscaping for wildlife and learning.

A wildlife habitat site will be your legacy to awareness and learning for many years into the future. Welcome to this exciting wildlife action project!

Introduction

A Project Rationale

"It is inconceivable to me that an ethical relation to land can exist without love, respect and admiration for land and a high regard for its value."

Aldo Leopold, The Land Ethic

Introduction
A Project Rationale

Are you ready to tackle a challenging venture that will make a difference for you and the future of wildlife?

THE HABITAT ENHANCEMENT ADVANTAGE

Whether your schoolyard is one paved acre or a 100-acre forested site, this outdoor resource can provide you and your students with a unique learning experience. You can benefit from both the process of developing a habitat enhancement project and the resulting outdoor classroom. At the same time, you can influence positive change for wildlife.

Safety issues, logistical concerns, or feelings of anxiety on the part of teachers often lead to an under utilized schoolyard. You can use this space successfully with the right ideas and guidance. Though not a quick and simple task, enhancing wildlife habitat in your schoolyard is an exciting and manageable project, providing challenges and rewards. Students and teachers can explore, discover and learn with every season.

Where is the Wildlife?

When we hear the word "wildlife," we often think of creatures we rarely see, like eagles, otters, bear, and moose. If you happen to live in a rural area, some of these animals may be part of your schoolyard wildlife. But for most of us, schoolyard life seems to have no "wild" side; animals are something we must go elsewhere to see.

Despite the notion that wildlife lives somewhere beyond our towns and cities, a typical neighborhood will have more than 25 kinds of birds and mammals, including squirrels, song birds, hawks, raccoons, and even foxes. These animals we take for granted are as much wildlife as eagles and moose, and you don't have to go to the wilderness to enjoy them. They are as close as your own schoolyard.

Wildlife in the Schoolyard

Wildlife can be as small as the smallest microscopic organisms, or as big as a whale, and includes birds, mammals, fish, insects, spiders, reptiles, and amphibians. This is important to remember when you consider the differences between schoolyard sites. Urban, suburban, and rural sites each will provide habitat for different wildlife species — some larger, others smaller, some familiar, and others less so.

You and your students can enhance your particular schoolyard to attract and support those species that are appropriate to your site. Enhancing habitat is one of the best ways we can help ensure wildlife's future.

VALUES OF HABITAT ENHANCEMENT PROJECTS

Sharing Habitats — Wildlife and Human Influence

No human action is without its consequences. The land that supports wildlife is also the land we use to farm, grow trees for wood products, and build our homes and businesses. These activities affect the quantity and quality of wildlife habitat. By carefully considering the needs of wildlife, we can have a positive influence on those species with which we share the land.

Diversity is the key to healthy populations, including our own. Providing habitat for a wide variety of species ensures our own health as well as the health of the natural system. Your schoolyard property — no matter how big or small — can support wildlife, and you can influence the abundance and variety found there.

Whole Learning and Integrated Teaching

Look at your schoolyard through the eyes of a child. Is it diverse, exciting and filled with different habitats and a multitude of wildlife? Or is it a monotonous sea of grass or blacktop?

"Habitat projects fit in with our mapping and earth resoures study in the fall."
KATHI MITCHELL, KIMBALL SCHOOL, CONCORD, NH

A young and growing mind will thrive in an environment that supports a diversity of wildlife. By enhancing the schoolyard site for wildlife, children can have real-life learning experiences as they discover the natural world and their role in it. This process becomes more meaningful when you involve them in every step.

The students will see tangible results from their work. As you involve the whole child in cognitive and affective learning experiences, those with different learning styles and skills will be able to achieve success.

This is also an excellent opportunity to develop cooperative learning systems, with students from each grade participating in mentorship groups, and teachers from different subject areas integrating their lessons.

More than Science

Though "nature" is considered a topic for science study, environmental education is, by definition, interdisciplinary. You can involve teachers and students from throughout your school.

For example, mapping your site will involve an understanding of geography. Estimating the size of outdoor areas will require basic math skills. Recording data and describing the site will utilize good writing skills. Planning changes in the schoolyard will involve learning about the study of uses, and some economics as well.

You, the Teacher

By initiating and carrying out this project with your students, you also benefit. The outdoors is accessible, and doesn't require special tools or transportation to study. Projects for wildlife habitat enhancement allow you to incorporate a variety of strategies, approaches, topics, and experiences within the curriculum.

You don't need to know all the answers, or even be a science teacher. Being in the outdoors will inspire learning on the part of your students, and you can find the specific information you need from resources in the Appendices. You and your students can learn together, drawing upon the knowledge and expertise of your fellow teachers and professionals in the field.

As you are exploring your space, planning and carrying out projects, and enjoying the results, you will have created the basis for daily lesson plans that can continue year-round. If you plan accordingly, this effort will continue year after year with new students, providing opportunities for more enhancement projects and maintenance of the original plan, and continued development of the outdoor classroom.

"There was a lot of personal gratification and kid culture at work. The students who took charge were a surprise."
SALLY COLLETE, PIERMONT SCHOOL PIERMONT, NH

Additional Benefits

There are many added benefits of wildlife habitat enhancement.

Aesthetic: Schoolyard landscaping is more often intended to enhance aesthetic quality rather than support wildlife. Bringing food and cover plantings into your schoolyard will not only serve on a practical level to feed and house wildlife, but will also enhance the natural beauty and aesthetic quality of the property.

Ecological: A diverse landscape, with many plant species, supports an abundance of wildlife. By increasing the number of plant species, you can increase the ecological stability of your schoolyard while creating important food and cover. Such habitats are less vulnerable to large-scale destruction by insect pests and diseases.

Economic: Landscaping for wildlife presents an opportunity to reduce heating and cooling costs for your school. And it adds economic value to the surrounding area.

The consideration you extend to wildlife on the schoolyard site will be increasingly rewarded each year, as you discover new wild visitors and enrich your lives with an awareness of the creatures that share this environment. In all these ways, a wildlife enhancement project repays your investment many times over. Just as important, landscaping for wildlife is fun.

WILDLIFE MANAGEMENT AND YOUR PROJECT

Taking action for wildlife is wildlife management. Management is based on an understanding of certain ecological concepts that allows us to manipulate them (these concepts will be discussed in Chapter 2). The changes that result may be positive or negative, depending on your perspective. Habitat, wildlife, and people are the three principal factors in wildlife management.

This practice began in the 19th century and continues today with such agencies as the U.S. Fish and Wildlife Service, state wildlife resource departments, the Cooperative Extension Service, and many independent conservation organizations.

Reduction and destruction of habitats are the most severe problems currently facing individual wildlife species. By manipulating habitat components (food, water, cover, space, and arrangement) wildlife managers work to develop and maintain habitat conditions suitable to species that can benefit from and cause benefit to a particular area. They may increase the population of a particular species, or encourage the greatest number and diversity of species possible in an area.

Wildlife managers also work with landowners to create and maintain habitat, reduce pollution and environmental degradation, and promote and enforce laws that protect habitats and animals from careless destruction. You can draw on their expertise to assist in developing your school's habitat enhancement plan, as you will see in Chapter 5.

Material for this chapter excerpted or adapted with permission from:

Henderson, Carrol L. 1987. *Landscaping for Wildlife*. Minnesota Department of Natural Resources, St. Paul.

Washington Department of Wildlife. *Urban Wildlife Series: Landscape Design for Wildlife*. Booklet

---

ENHANCING YOUR SCHOOLYARD FOR WILDLIFE OFFERS MANY BENEFITS:

Wildlife Habitat
- Provides more wildlife food and cover.
- Promotes pollination.

Ecological Benefits
- Increases plant and animal diversity with greater ecological stability.
- Keeps the environment free of pesticides and herbicides.
- Lessens the effects of global warming.
- Adds oxygen to the atmosphere.
- Recycles plant nutrients.

Water Resources
- Promotes local groundwater recharge.
- Helps prevent soil erosion.

Aesthetic Appeal
- Promotes change and variety throughout the seasons.
- Increases wildlife viewing opportunities.

Economic
- Conserves energy resources.
- Reduces heating and cooling costs.

Maintenance
- Requires less labor, money, time, and consumption of fossil fuels.
- Reduces the need for fertilization.

Management
- Uses disease-resistant and climate-adapted native vegetation.
- Increases natural diversity, helping control pest populations.

Section I
Laying the Groundwork

"It is fortunate, perhaps, that no matter how intently one studies the hundred little dramas of the woods and meadows, one can never learn all of the salient facts about any one of them."

Aldo Leopold, The Land Ethic

Chapter 1
Getting Started

Whether you are planting one tree or planning a large-scale habitat enhancement effort, this guide will assist you in defining and meeting your objectives.

INTRODUCING: THE PROJECT HOME GUIDE

The guide is divided into sections that correspond to the phases you will go through in planning and caring for a schoolyard wildlife enhancement project. Each chapter includes:

> Background information
> "How to" instructions and tools
> Supplemental, multi-disciplinary student activities
> References
> Checklists

Introductory activities will help you and your students understand the basic concepts of habitat. We've also included hands-on activities and projects, such as mapping exercises, to guide you in working through each step of the project.

How to Use this Guide

This guide includes a substantial amount of material. We've used highlights to make it easier for you to access the information you need.

Read through the guide, become generally familiar with the processes described, and consider how the recommendations fit into your particular situation. Then, when you are ready to begin your habitat enhancement project, return to each section for the detailed information.

You may find you have already reached the stage of assessing your schoolyard site, or you and your students may have devised a strategy for enhancement. Step into the process where it is appropriate for you to do so. Select the parts that apply to your situation and supplement with other materials from the resource list.

Sections:
Section 1, Chapters 1-2: Pre-activity

This section will familiarize you with the project, and with wildlife needs and how they are combined to provide habitat, so you will have a good idea of what you are trying to achieve before you begin. This information is key to your success.

Section ll, Chapters 3-4: Planning

As a planning guide for enhancing wildlife habitat, this section explains how to analyze the existing conditions in your schoolyard, and how to use this information in your plan. It lists and describes principles to guide your planning and to help you structure enhancement projects.

Section lll, Chapters 5-6: Action

Included here are suggestions for a variety of enhancement projects, and guidelines for developing and implementing your enhancement plan.

Section IV, Chapters 7-8: Follow-up

In these chapters you'll find guidelines for maintenance plans, as well as activity ideas for the outdoor classroom on your schoolyard site.

Section V, Appendices A-K: Supplemental Information

The appendices provide detailed information, including: recommended plants for your area, plans for building projects, a sampler of activities with source listing, and materials resources. For any topic you wish to study in greater depth, there is a listing of where to find further information or assistance.

BEFORE YOU TAKE ON THIS PROJECT...

Consider Your Site

School sites vary according to size, variety of habitat types, amount of open space and surrounding area. Not every school site can attract the same species of wildlife.

Consider at the outset: What are the realistic possibilities for your site?

Are there enormous possibilities for improvements, or limited possibilities? Do you expect to be in the same school for awhile, or will there be a new school building with new possibilities in the near future?

Refer to Chapter 2 for a description of different habitat types in schoolyards. Appendix C contains information on regional habitat types and the wildlife that occur there.

Setting Goals – Making the Commitment

Know generally what your goals are before you set out. In Chapter 4, you will be detailing these goals with respect to individual projects. For now, decide if you want to invest a smaller amount of energy and time over several years, or a great deal of time over a full year. Remember, once you make the commitment to wildlife enhancement, maintenance and

---

"The project taught us about our property at the new school site. It extended beyond what we had expected."

NANCY SANDELL PIERMONT
SCHOOL PIERMONT, NH

THE PROJECT - A MASTER PLAN OVERVIEW

1) Build a school-wide team.
2) Make a map of your schoolyard site.
3) Assess your schoolyard with a site inventory.
4) Evaluate the inventory.
5) Set your goals and objectives.
7) Develop your plan.
8) Implement your enhancement projects.
9) Maintain your site.
10) Evaluate your project's success.

development of the projects should be expected to continue for the long-term. This is an investment of time and energy, and will continue indefinitely.

Student Driven Action

What can the students do? Everything in this guide has been designed for the students to accomplish with your assistance. There are grade-level appropriate activities provided throughout the process, so students in each grade will be able to participate in every step.

Younger students will learn a simpler version of concepts and take on smaller projects, while older students will carry out the more complex mapping and planning work. For example, while first graders will be able to compare maple leaves with pine needles, and recognize and point out the differences, sixth graders will be able to distinguish between groups of deciduous and evergreen trees, and can learn to identify several species of each. Both of these learning experiences and contributions are valid and valuable to the process of identifying and enhancing wildlife habitat.

Working with your students through this process will be more time-consuming than arranging for a resource manager to come and assess your property. While schedule demands may seem to necessitate the latter, *we strongly recommend you involve the students on every level.* That way, they will have ownership of the project, and will gain a greater understanding of wildlife. In addition, the entire process will be a learning experience.

Even with the students actively involved, you may choose to seek assistance from technical professionals in the field. Refer to Appendix G for a resource listing.

Making the Student Connection

If the students are to drive this project, they need to be excited about it. At the end of the chapter are several activities to

> "Our 6th grade students did the mapping and measuring in small groups, and the entire 6th grade participated in the tree planting."
> JANE WELCH
> KIMBALL SCHOOL
> CONCORD, NH

GENERAL SITE CONSIDERATIONS

A. Physical
   1. Overall size of area.
   2. Land use on areas surrounding school site.
   3. Budgetary considerations for development and maintenance of outdoor school site structures.
B. Education
   1. Grade level/age range of school students.
   2. Curriculum requirements and needs.
   3. Current and projected use of outdoor school sites in curriculum.
   4. Administrative/instructional backing and support of school site use.
   5. Budgetary considerations for educational use of outdoor school sites.
C. Socio-Cultural
   1. Socio-economic aspects of surrounding/supporting community.
   2. Use of school site for non-school functions/purposes.

Prepared by Jerry Schierloh, Associate Professor of Environmental Studies, NJ School of Conservation. Documents from Graduate Course:"Ourdoor Teaching Sites for Environmental Education," Montclair State College

TEAM BUILDING

Involve your students in this process.

- Ground the project in student leadership.
  Have them choose the projects and make the effort with your leadership and guidance.

- Have a clear goal.
  Start small. Make the goal realistic and reachable.

- Gather support within the school: other teachers, administrators, maintenance staff, Board of Education. Inform them of your plans, invite their advice and consult with them.

- Garner community and parent support.

- Establish a working group and an advisory committee to provide leadership, direction, and help avoid pitfalls.

- Make the curriculum connections.

- Support the students' efforts to accomplish their projects.

- Establish a support group: environmental professionals, local businesses, clubs, youth groups, service organizations, and communications media.

(Adapted with permission from WILD School Sites: A Guide to Preparing for Habitat Improvement Projects on School Grounds. 1993, Western Regional Environmental Education Council)

help them develop initial awareness of the schoolyard site, and begin making the project personally relevant.

Building a Working Team

Before you begin the work in and around your schoolyard site, you will want the assistance and support of certain people in your school. It is fundamental to your success that you build a working team, consisting of yourself, the students, teachers from other subject areas and grades, the school administrator and, above all, the custodial staff.

A team serves several purposes. First, it ensures that you will not have to accomplish this project solo. You will have the expertise, assistance, and person-power for labor that other individuals in your school can provide. Second, you will be far more certain your students' efforts to improve habitat will not be inadvertently dismantled or mown down, and that your maintenance plans will be supported in the event some team members leave the school.

A second facet of the working team is the support provided by your community. Parents, local businesses, and community service organizations can all provide you with invaluable support — in funding, materials, expertise, and labor.

Team Players

Who might you involve, and what will they do? Begin by creating the working team within the school, and make it as large as you need to accomplish the project you are considering.

You, *the teacher,* are the mentor who facilitates the process.

The *students* provide real leadership; consider a representative from each class involved.

Faculty make the curriculum connections with the subjects they teach.

Maintenance staff often knows the grounds better than anyone, so their assistance gives them a sense of ownership; they can provide access for students to materials, equipment, and expertise.

Keep the *school administrator* informed of progress.

Parent/community representatives help to instill a sense of pride by helping the community see the value of the project.

Real Examples of Team Building:

Piermont Village School, Piermont, NH is a small, rural elementary school, located on a new site in 1992. Teachers from each grade set up small, cross-teaching groups of their students, grades 1-6. The older students presented the results of their planning efforts to the PTA, which rewarded them with funding support.

North Hampton Elementary School, North Hampton, NH advertised their enhancement plan in their area, including a write-up in a newsletter to 2000 families. A local hospital, marking its 100th anniversary with a community-wide celebration, donated 25 maple trees to the school.

A teacher-aide at **Ossipee Central School, Center Ossipee, NH** contributed her skills as a professional landscaper to their wildlife habitat project. The school had plans to expand the original building on a neighboring property. The aide transplanted several larger trees which would otherwise have been destroyed to make room for the new wing. She also helped design a formal wildlife garden for the community.

The coordinator of S.T.E.P (Special Training for Employment Program) at **White Mountain Regional High School, Whitefield, NH** enlisted the assistance of several wildlife professionals. He contacted the Audubon Society of New Hampshire for information on bluebird box placement and the use of boxes by other bird species. And he invited the county forester to visit the site to advise them about plantings.

Fundraising – Enlisting Financial Support

You will need financial support from within the community and/or the school to carry out your habitat enhancement plans. Most sources of support are more willing to donate services or materials than money. Once you've established your enhancement plan (see Chapter 5), you can better determine what you will need.

"The students made a presentation to the school board and conservation society, and received matching funds for our project."

EILEEN BELYEA
PIERMONT SCHOOL
PIERMONT, NH

FUNDRAISING TIPS

- Consider writing grant proposals.
- Word-of-mouth is your best advertisement.
- Let people know the project is up for adoption.
- Approach businesses, civic groups, and other organizations with the opportunity to contribute.
- Give parents a variety of opportunities to donate time, materials, expertise, and encouragement.
- Advertise projects through local media including radio and television.
- Don't forget fundraising events.

(Adapted with permission from WILD School Sites: A Guide to Preparing for Habitat Improvement Projects on School Grounds,1993, Western Regional Environmental Education Council)

Begin with some type of "wish list" of items. This list will result in the forming of a budget and time-table. Once this has been developed, you will be ready to begin a fund drive.

Start fund raising with a sure thing, such as a group or individual that has previously given to the school. Remember to tell them exactly what you want, how much it costs and how you will use it to benefit the students, both now and in the future.

When approaching organizations or individuals for money, keep in mind they are often competing with each other for recognition. If you can secure funds from one group you have cleared a major obstacle. When you approach other potential funding sources, let them know you have committed funds and identify who has given them. The competition between groups may swing the decision in your favor.

You may be more successful if you ask for portions of the funds instead of asking for everything from one source. You may also request materials, such as plants, gravel, and lumber. It is often easier for a company to donate materials than money.

A final note: When a group gives you funds, give them publicity in return. Whether it is a sign, newspaper article, or just word of mouth, they will appreciate and remember it the next time you ask for something.

Media and Public Relations

Providing the media with news releases and photography about your projects helps you gain public support and encouragement, and can extend awareness and appreciation of environmental issues in the community. Don't forget to publicize your activities in a school newsletter, slide show, hallway display, store window, or other means within your local school community of teachers, parents, and students.

Have at least two people on the working team be responsible for media and public relations. Here are some guidelines:

1. Make parent-teacher organizations aware of projects and get them involved monetarily and physically.

2. Send flyers home with children, explaining proposed projects and inviting parent involvement.

3. Send flyers or call/visit landowners adjacent to schoolgrounds to explain projects and their purposes.

4. Contact local media to photograph and interview your all-day work/ construction session or big planting days with children. Prepare and send a media information packet in advance.

5. On days you expect the media, have a fact sheet explaining what you are doing that day and why. Be specific about the features of the outdoor classroom and, if possible, have children working.

6. Make team members available for service group luncheons or meeting presentations. Short slide presentations are helpful to illustrate the project.

(Adapted with permission from So You Want to Start an Outdoor Classroom... Compiled and edited by: Oklahoma Conservation Commission and Oklahoma Department of Wildlife Conservation.)

Uninvited Visitors

Together wildlife and humans share the same living space, or habitat. Wildlife need habitat that humans, through development, provide, alter or destroy. Wildlife populations in turn respond in both positive and negative manners to these habitat changes.

When humans and wildlife need the same resources from an area, a conflict may arise, and the wildlife involved labeled 'pests'. Conflicts can be minimized through proper planning, management, and by noting how alterations will affect particular species.

This project is intended to enhance habitat for a variety of wildlife species, and to learn to live with and appreciate them on your schoolyard site. With this in mind, it is wise to remember that the notion of "nuisance wildlife" or "pests" is relative to your needs and expectations, and is different in the eyes of different people. In an urban area, your greatest success in attracting wildlife may be to provide habitat for starlings, pigeons, and squirrels, which are sometimes considered pests. Consider this aspect of wildlife as you set out.

See Chapter 6 for information on "Troubleshooting" – getting the wildlife you want.

"In order to generate some curiosity about the project, my students and I picked a school to write to about the fun times and explain the activities. In return, we would get input, questions, inquiries about our habitat progress from our HOME pen pals."

PAUL OUIMET, S.T.E.P.
WHITE MOUNTAIN
REGIONAL HIGH SCHOOL
WHITEFIELD, NH

POSSIBLE FUNDING SOURCES

School PTA	Local Conservation Clubs
Endowment Program	Local Foundations
Individual School's Budget	Local Businesses
School Corporation Board	Corporations
Soil & Water Conservation District	Garden Clubs
County Farm Bureau Group	Raffles/Bake Sales
Local Service Clubs & Organizations	Collect Items to Recycle
Resource Management Agencies	Federal & State Grants

(Reprinted with permission from Guidelines and Features for Outdoor Classrooms, Indiana Department of Natural Resources, Division of Forestry.)

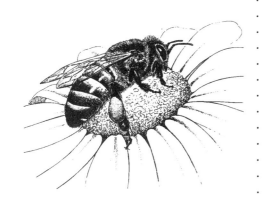

Maintenance

Your projects will need to be maintained throughout the seasons, when school is not in session, and over the long term. This is a critical component to the successful continuation of your wildlife habitat enhancement efforts.

Plan to have a network of teachers, students and custodians involved to cover the job of maintenance, such as watering plantings and keeping feeders filled. Involve your school's maintenance and custodial staff as key team members. Much of your efforts can be unintentionally undone by uninformed custodial staff carrying out their daily tasks.

See Chapter 7 for details on specific maintenance concerns and developing a maintenance plan.

Safety Precautions

Taking your students outside can seem like a big risk for teachers. Children will be naturally excited with the unusual class setting if this is new for them.

Establish parameters before you set out, and invite the participation of other adults, parent volunteers, or high school student helpers who can supervise. You may wish to divide the students into work groups. Give them specifically outlined directions and tasks, and well-defined areas in which to work.

See Chapter 4 for details on precautions you should take for the safety of students and wildlife.

✎ MASTER PLAN CHECKLIST:

The process of preparing an enhancement plan has four main steps:

❑ I. Assemble information about your schoolyard and your school's needs. (Chapters 3 and 4)

1. Map and inventory the site. Record the major natural and human features. Identify components of habitat on the site: food, water, cover and their overall arrangement.

2. Research past history of the site. The natural and human features you find could give clues to what plants and animals might have been there before changes took place.

3. Identify needs. What is needed for people? For the school? For wildlife? For the community?

❑ **II Compare your findings with wildlife information to determine what your site can support. (Chapter 4 and Appendices C and D)**

4. Compile and analyze your results. What do you have? This will give you a basis for understanding what kind of habitat conditions could exist there as a result of your project.

5. Determine what species the site can support. Compare your findings with area wildlife habitat information. Develop a species list.

❑ **III. Set objectives to meet the needs of your school and the wildlife you want to attract. (Chapter 5)**

6. Develop the project goals and objectives. Include a list of the outcomes you anticipate. Briefly describe the value of this project to people, the school, wildlife, and the community.

7. Choose the animal and plant species you want to attract and/or enhance, as well as the plant species needed to improve the site as a habitat for the wildlife you identify.

❑ **IV. Determine what kind of habitat plantings and other projects you will have to meet your objectives, and where they will go. (Chapter 6)**

8. List and describe the methods and strategies you will use to accomplish the project goals and objectives. This is the most detailed part of the management plan.

TIPS FOR SUCCESS:

- Break projects into small steps, to see improvement and change over a short time.
- Emphasize early success, to build interest and momentum.
- Complete projects over an extended time, to use resources as they become available.
- Plan a work day on site — possibly around an environmental calendar event like Earth Day, Arbor Day, or the solstices — to inform and involve the community and get things done.
- Communicate, stressing the values of the project, to get everyone involved.
- Adopt allies who can help get the word out.
- Develop a mentoring program. Match groups of students with willing volunteers who can share knowledge and skills, or consider cross-teaching with older and younger students working together.
- Recruit parent and other community volunteers.
- Remember maintenance. Take steps to maintain the site for the long term.
- Prepare students to give presentations and tours of the school site.
- Approach businesses, civic groups, and other organizations with the opportunity to contribute.
- Advertise projects through local media, including radio and television.
- Don't forget fund-raiser events.
- Consider writing grant proposals.
- Think creatively.

(Adapted with permission from WILD School Sites: A Guide to Preparing for Wildlife Improvement Projects on School Grounds, 1993, Western Regional Environmental Education Council)

"We feel a real need for community involvement, and are seeking ways to make that happen."

SARAH BARNES
OSSIPEE CENTRAL SCHOOL
CENTER OSSIPEE, NH

9. List and describe the resources that will be needed to accomplish the plan. What people, money, materials, equipment, etc. are needed?

10. Develop a working timeline and calendar. Identify the priorities. Include all the steps from planning the project, to accomplishing the specific habitat improvement, and then maintaining it over time. Plan for short and long term.

11. List ways you will evaluate and measure the project's success, including its affects on student learning.

12. List and describe the steps you will take to involve support groups and communications media.

Whenever possible, plan for ways to include diverse input. Members of the advisory committee should be a good source of varied advice.

Note: These steps may be rearranged, lengthened or shortened to fit your particular case. Tailor the checklist to make it most effective for you.

Adapted with permission from WILD School Sites: A Guide to Preparing for Habitat Improvement Projects on School Grounds, *1993, Western Regional Environmental Education Council, and Landscaping for Wildlife, Henderson, Carrol L., 1987*

✍ EARLY AWARENESS ACTIVITIES

25 Words

Materials:
Paper/pencil

Procedure:
After investigating all parts of your schoolyard site, try to come up with 25 words which best describe the area.

If you wish, you may group these words into categories, such as:

Words about the ENTIRE AREA

Words about MUCH of the AREA

Words about PARTS of the AREA

Words about ISOLATED POCKETS of the AREA

An On-the-Spot Story

Materials:
Paper/pencil

Procedure:
1. Imagine you are a person who just came to the site from a place far away from here. You know nothing about the site, other than what you can piece together from any visible evidence.

2. Using such evidence from the entire designated area, write a short story (500 words or less) about what you think possibly could have happened on this site.

3. Notes:

— The characters and events of this story can include both living and non-living things.

— As much as possible, try to give the events of your story a "chronological" order, a proper sequence in time.

— Your story can begin as far back as you wish to take it, concluding with the present time.

— Use only visible evidence, rather than information gathered from other people or printed materials.

Colors

Materials:
Box of crayons, paper/pencil

Procedure:
1. Using the box of crayons, try to match as many as possible to the colors of things found on the schoolyard site.

2. Label each of the shades discovered with the name of the feature or material that is close to that color. You may want to record your discoveries on two separate charts, one for Natural Features, and the other for Human-made Features.

3. Decide what colors were the most common.

4. If you were going to add additional human-made features to the schoolyard site, which colors would you select that would best blend with the existing environment?

(Activities from Jerry Schierloh, Associate Professor of Environmental Studies, NJ School of Conservation, for Graduate Course: "Outdoor Teaching Sites for Environmental Education," Montclair State College.)

Additional Activities from Project WILD
    Wildlife is Everywhere
    Wild Words
    Animal Poetry

from Project Learning Tree
Adopt a Tree, with extensions for writing, drawing, finding your tree

Material for this chapter excerpted or adapted with permission from:
   Carmen, Sam, ed. *Guidelines and Features for Outdoor Classrooms*, Indiana Department of Natural Resources, Division of Forestry

Henderson, Carrol L. 1987. *Landscaping for Wildlife*. 144 pp. Minnesota Department of Natural Resources, St. Paul

Leedy, D.L. and L.W. Adams. 1984. *A Guide to Urban Wildlife Management*. National Institute for Urban Wildlife, Columbia, MD.

Living with Wildlife, developed by the Illinois Department of Conservation in cooperation with the Illinois State Board of Education. Adapted from the U.S. Fish and Wildlife Service and National Institute for Urban Wildlife "Wildlife Habitat Conservation Teacher's Pacs."

*So You Want to Start an Outdoor Classroom...*Compiled and edited by: Oklahoma Conservation Commission and Oklahoma Department of Wildlife Conservation.

Jerry Schierloh, Associate Professor of Environmental Studies, NJ School of Conservation. Documents from Graduate Course *"Outdoor Teaching Sites for Environmental Education"* (Montclair State College)

WILD School Sites: A Guide to Preparing for Wildlife Improvement Projects on School Grounds. 1993, Western Regional Environmental Education Council

Chapter 2
Learning About Wildlife and Habitat

A crucial step towards improving wildlife habitat on your schoolyard site is understanding the needs of the animals you want to attract. If you keep these needs in mind as you develop a plan, you will have an excellent chance for success.

THE WORLD OF HABITAT

What do we have in common with bears, loons, snakes and caterpillars? We all need a place we can call "home" in order to survive. Four basic components make up a healthy home — food, water, cover (or shelter), and space — arranged so we can make the most of each.

The size and health of a wildlife population is largely determined by these available resources, collectively referred to as the animal's habitat. Although there may be considerable overlap in the habitat requirements of two or more similar species, each has its own unique requirements.

Optimum habitat for one species may not be optimum for another. The gray squirrel uses acorns for food, while the woodpecker eats insects, although both live in the treetops. Mallards use thick grass and forb (herbaceous) cover for nesting, while wood ducks nest in tree cavities.

All four basic needs must be met within an area in the proper arrangement, or the species will not exist there. For example, even though woodlands offer water, brushy cover, and abundant space, you wouldn't expect to find a woodchuck living there since the food it depends on — mostly grasses — is found in fields.

- Wildlife have four basic needs for survival: food, water, cover (shelter), and space.

- Human beings share the same basic needs as wildlife.

- Managing habitat types, as opposed to managing specific species, allows us to improve habitat, benefiting more wildlife species.

Special Needs

Habitat requirements for wildlife change during the seasons of the year. The food they eat in the winter may be very different from what is consumed in the summer. The cover they need for nesting may be quite different from the cover needed to survive a winter storm. Needs also may change with the sex and age of the animal.

Many wildlife species have special ways of meeting their four basic needs. To avoid a winter scarcity of food, for example, some animals hibernate, others migrate to other food sources, while others store food. Some species may require certain conditions of temperature, salinity, humidity, intensity of light, or other factors, in addition to the four basic needs.

Dynamic Habitat

As you work toward developing a habitat enhancement program, keep in mind that habitat is dynamic. Over time, habitats of wildlife are subject to change, whether by natural forces such as floods, fires, volcanic eruptions, earthquakes, windstorms, disease and insects, or by human activities. Any change in the environment, whether natural or human-caused, affects wildlife.

At the end of this chapter, you'll find a listing of Project WILD activities to help you teach these concepts to your students.

HABITAT COMPONENTS

Food

All animals must eat other animals and/or plants to survive. Inadequate food supplies on your schoolyard site could limit the presence of a desired species, even if that species is native to your area.

Vegetation, in particular, is of critical importance to wildlife, for both food and cover (shelter). Loss of vegetation worldwide appears to be one of the greatest threats to wildlife, as well as to humans.

Several types of plant foods can be provided by an enhancement effort, including fruits and berries, grains and seeds, nectar sources, nuts and acorns, browse plants (woody twigs and buds), forage plants (grasses and legumes) and aquatic plants. Though we usually think of nuts and berries as the primary wildlife foods, all parts and kinds of plants are used.

Some animals eat a great variety of food items; others eat only a few types of food. The diets of most animals change with the seasons, as different foods become available and as their needs vary.

Mast — the fruit of nut-bearing trees, such as acorns from oak trees or beechnuts from beech trees — is a good example of periodically abundant food. Squirrels and bluejays store acorns for later use; deer and bear develop a thick layer of fat (stored energy for winter), through feeding on

---

HABITAT IS...

- Food – seeds, berries, nuts, flower nectar, insects.
- Water – birdbaths, drip faucets, sprinklers, ponds, puddles, streams.
- Cover – trees, shrubs, brush piles, rock piles, hollow logs, snags.
- Space – quiet space, open space, corridors, territories.

Reprinted with permission from Washington Dept. of Wildlife Urban Wildlife Series: Landscape Design for Wildlife, Booklet.

nuts in the fall. Seasonally abundant berry crops are also attractive and important to wildlife.

Providing habitat for animals which are prey for other animals can attract predators to your site. In this way you are influencing the food chain.Air and water support an astounding variety of insects that are scooped up by birds and bats, or eaten by water dwellers such as frogs and turtles. The insects we may regard as pests or annoyances are really a lifeline for many wildlife species. Wildlife play a key role in keeping insect populations in check.

See Appendices D and E for information on wildlife food preferences and the care of food and cover plantings.

Water

Water — springs, beaver ponds, marshes, creeks, swamps, lakes, and rivers — is a vital component of our environment. Though not all kinds of animals need standing water, water is an essential requirement for all wildlife. Some get the water they need from their food or the dew. Some require water for special needs during certain phases of their life cycle. Amphibians, for example, need water for the development of their eggs and young, and most birds need to be near water when nesting.

For those species requiring standing water, a creek, spring, small pond, or even an artificial fountain or birdbath serves the purpose. A healthy habitat provides for the year-round water needs of wildlife, as well as corridors or travelways to water from areas of cover.

Cover (or Shelter)

Cover is the protective element within an animal's habitat. Most wildlife will not stay for long in unprotected sites where they are exposed and vulnerable to predation or extreme weather conditions. Birds and other animals constantly seek protective cover, whether they are foraging for food, taking care of their young, or simply resting.

Cover may be a hedgerow for a rabbit or a spruce tree for a golden-crowned kinglet. Regardless of form, it provides for one or more of the necessary functions in the lives of animals: breeding, nesting, hiding, loafing, sleeping, feeding, and traveling.

Many migrating bird species seek heavily vegetated areas as stopover resting and feeding sites. Warblers, vireos, flycatchers, tanagers, and buntings pass through in spring and fall. These brilliant messengers of the seasons may take advantage of cover provided on your schoolyard site.

Vegetation like trees, shrubs, grasses and flowers, structures like rockpiles and brushpiles, slow water, and burrows in the ground are just some of the forms of protective cover used by wildlife. Tall grasses, dense shrubs,

"Speakers during Earth Week covered some of the concept information for our project, building awareness."

RACHEL WARD
OSSIPEE CENTRAL SCHOOL
CENTER OSSIPEE, NH

leaf litter on the ground, evergreen boughs, high leafy tree canopies, downed logs, stumps, and cavities in decaying trees all provide valuable cover for a variety of wildlife, as do bird houses, bridges, and abandoned buildings.

Corridors

All animals have to get from one place to another — daily movement in search of food, or seasonal migration to wintering or breeding grounds. Terrestrial animals, such as rabbits, fox and deer, use hedgerows, stream beds, and ravines in their daily and nightly forays. Their survival depends on undisturbed travel lanes or corridors that have an abundance of vegetative cover, like brushy fence rows or hedgerows.

A woodlot isolated from other woodlands by open fields is a habitat "island," which may have fewer species of wildlife than nearby woodlands. The variety of species found in such a woodlot depends upon many things, but a major factor is its accessibility to animals from other areas. Vegetative corridors provide not only travel lanes, but also habitat for species like catbirds, cardinals, pheasants and rabbits, which are adapted to such areas.

Space

Space, or home range, is the area occupied by an individual, a family group or a social group, within which the needs for food, water and cover can be met. The size of this living space depends on body size and food habits. Consequently, certain wildlife need more space than others. A few square feet may be adequate for a field mouse, while a bear may need a few thousand acres.

In the context of your schoolyard efforts, space will be limited to the number of acres you plan to enhance. Many species require large areas to meet all their needs, which may exceed the boundaries of your site.

Assuming that space will be limiting to some degree, your activities should focus on the enhancement of the quality and availability of food, water, and cover. An animal's requirements for space may diminish as other habitat requirements are improved.

Arrangement

Habitat components must be arranged to be accessible to the animal. Often, creating the correct arrangement or juxtaposition of food, cover and water is a

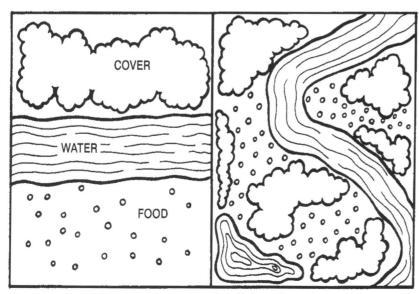

Poor interspersion of habitat components

Good interspersion; same acreage arranged so more wildlife can access them key to making your schoolyard site more attractive to wildlife. This "correct" arrangement depends on the species you want to attract.

Sometimes existing food and cover occur in separate areas. In this case, an important strategy may be to provide cover near the existing food, or vice versa. Some food plants also serve as cover, like shrubs for rabbits. Or cover plants may provide a forage base for other food items, such as insects on tree foliage.

RELATED WILDLIFE CONCEPTS

Diversity

In habitat, diversity is the spice of life. Different species of wildlife depend on different types of vegetation. Some species of wildlife depend on one vegetation type, such as the pine warbler in pine forests and the bobolink in a hay field. Other species, such as white-tailed deer, depend on a variety of vegetative types. Increasing the variety in vegetation types will result in a greater variety of wildlife.

The following add up to increased diversity:

Variety: A good mix of plants will attract many species of wildlife. Provide a variety of evergreen and deciduous trees and shrubs, young and old trees, and different seed-bearing, fruit-bearing, and nectar-producing shrubs and flowers.

Edges: The zone of change between two habitat types — for example, where trees and shrubs meet a meadow or stream — is called edge. A greater diversity in vegetative types results in more edge. On your site, mimic natural edges with layers of vegetation with curved and irregular borders — no straight lines. Pockets in the edge will provide more secluded hiding places for wildlife.

Layering: Naturally occurring plants grow in many layers, rather than at all the same height. Most species of wildlife feed, nest, or rest only at certain heights in these layers. Plant all the different layers of vegetation: ground cover, low shrubs, tall shrubs, small broadleaf trees, tall broadleaf trees, and tall conifers.

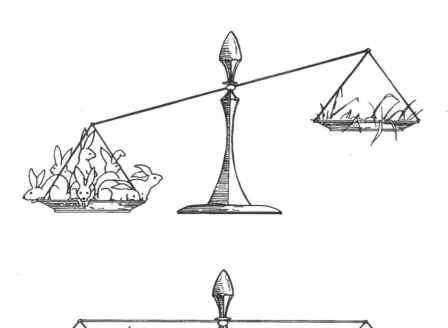

Carrying Capacity

There is a limit to how many animals can be sustained on an area of land over a period of time. That limit is called the habitat's carrying capacity, and is determined by the quantity and quality of food, water, cover and space.

An increase or decrease of one basic requirement can influence this limit. If the wildlife population is greater than the carrying capacity, the excess animals will die or leave.

Carrying capacity is not a constant number. It fluctuates in response to environmental influences. These may be naturally-occurring, such as trees taking over what was an open field, or human-induced, such as building a housing development in that field. It also varies from year to year and from season to season.

You can influence the carrying capacity of your schoolyard site for certain wildlife species by providing food, water, and cover.

Limiting Factor

The need that is in shortest supply, and therefore prevents the wildlife population from getting any larger, is called the limiting factor. For example, your site may include a pond that offers food, water, and space for wood ducks, but without cavity trees for cover, you wouldn't expect wood ducks to be nesting there. The limiting factor — in this case, cover —determines the habitat's carrying capacity.

Limiting factors are very important to wildlife management. If you want to increase a population, you have to determine what is holding it down. If it is lack of cover, providing more food won't help.

You can influence habitat to compensate for limiting factors by providing food, water and cover.

Until the section labelled "Cover" is raised, the container can't hold any more.

Plant Succession

Plant succession is the change of plant species on a piece of ground over a period of years.   Every acre of soil and water has a definite sequence in plant cover that occurs over time, called "successional stages," which occur in a cyclical pattern. We can usually predict the type of vegetation that will occur in each stage as an area proceeds through this cycle.

In general, the stages of plant succession that occur on land are:

      1. bare ground
      2. annual forbs and/or grasses
      3. perennial forbs and grasses
      4. shrubs
      5. young woodland or trees
      6. mature woodland or trees

A single step in this succession may take weeks, months, years, or even centuries, depending on a variety of natural and human-caused factors. If the land is disturbed at any time during this plant succession trend, succession will begin again.

STAGES OF PLANT SUCCESSION AND ASSOCIATED WILDLIFE SPECIES

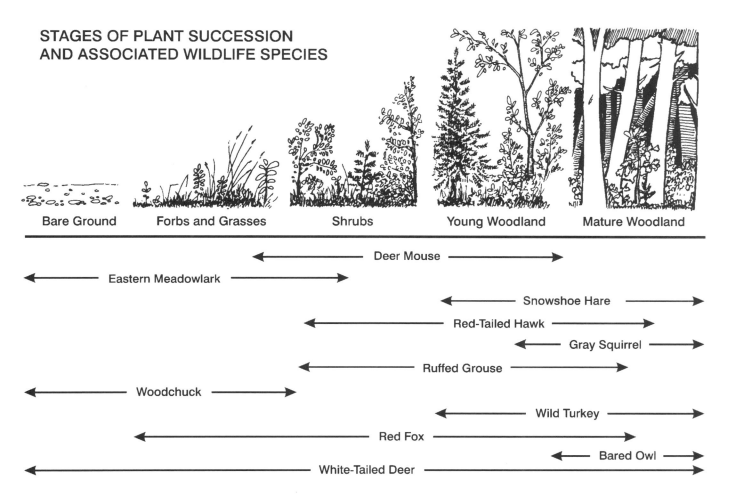

In some regions, soil or climate will prevent succession from proceeding past a certain stage. Other factors also cause this — lightning, fire, insect or disease outbreaks, tornadoes, hurricanes, ice, etc. However, humans most often are the agents that interrupt plant succession when we plow, mow or burn a field, cut timber, or clear brushy areas.

Different wildlife species prefer different stages of plant succession. You can encourage the wildlife species you're interested in by manipulating plant succession to suit the needs of those species. For example, regularly mowing a field will maintain the grassy vegetation.

In addition, many wildlife species need more than one successional stage to provide all their habitat requirements. Mixing plots of different successional stages within an area, a practice called interspersion , can support a greater variety of wildlife in an area.

HABITAT TYPES

Schools and their surrounding yards occur in urban, suburban and rural areas, and vary greatly in the size and type of available wildlife habitat. The characteristics of your schoolyard site will have a significant influence on the types of wildlife you can expect to attract, and on which projects make the most sense for your enhancement efforts.

For example, urban schools will be most successful attracting those species adapted to life in human communities, such as house sparrows, grey squirrels, and bats. Rural schoolyards may attract species such as snow-shoe hare or cottontail rabbit, which require the extensive open spaces or undisturbed places available in rural areas. Schools located in suburban areas may attract either of these types of wildlife, depending on the area surrounding the schoolyard.

Sample Schoolyard Habitats

These three New Hampshire schools have implemented habitat enhancement projects. All three sites have parking lots, and fields or grassy areas. Some have woodlands and wetlands. Each has a different acreage and different surrounding community, and each is located in a somewhat different climate zone.

Urban school site:

Kimball School, Concord, NH, is located near the center of the capital city on a 2-acre parcel of asphalt, peastone, and mud. It houses 350 students. A small grass patch in front of the building supports some landscaping of flowers, shrubs and trees. The combination recreation area and parking lot is surrounded on three sides by a stockade fence, some of which is lined with vegetation. A small dirt playground includes playground structures. Fourth graders conduct a hawk watch from the rooftop of the school building each fall.

Suburban school site:

McClelland Elementary School, Rochester, NH, is a large elementary school with over 600 students, located on 20 acres in a busy residential area. The two parking lots, large playing field, and 2 playgrounds with play structures are comprised of asphalt or packed dirt and grass. A new middle school behind McClelland has an access road circling it which bisects the playground. A large parcel of woodlands borders the entrance of the road, which runs along a field behind the elementary school. The school is separated from the residential area by a stockade fence. Students have planted trees and shrubs in front of the building around a circular driveway.

Rural school site:

White Mountain Regional High School, Whitefield, NH, stands on a 392-acre site in the White Mountains. This includes 318 acres of forested lands with a Christmas tree farm, apple orchard, and 10 acres of clearcut under a woodlands management program; 6 acres of pasture, 3 barns and a sugar house for vocational programs in forestry, agriculture, horticulture, and animal science; sports fields for baseball, soccer and field hockey; and a wetlands, road, and 200-car parking lot. The front of the school building is landscaped with shrubs and flower gardens. Students frequently have the opportunity to view deer, moose, beaver, and wild game birds.

Wildlife habitat includes both naturally-occurring and human-influenced areas. Some of these habitats occur on your schoolyard site:

> wetlands
> fields and meadows
> edges
> forest and woodlands
> courtyards
> gardens
> parking lots
> buildings and other structures

In Chapter 4, you will learn how to assess which habitats make up your schoolyard. Appendix C includes detailed information on regional habitat types.

"Two good things to focus on were the importance of habitat and human influences, both positive and negative, and the connection with geography and math in mapping."

BILL CARR
MILFORD ELEMENTARY
MILFORD, NH

✎ Your Habitat Checklist

Keep in mind the following principles when doing habitat enhancement work.

The four basic needs for a successful project are:

❏ Food: Every species has its own idea of what makes up a delicious meal. Ensure that food is available for the species you want to attract and your site will support.

❏ Water: Clean water from ponds, marshes, swamps, lakes and rivers means life for all creatures.

❏ Cover: Cover can be living or dead trees, shrubs, grasses, flowers, burrows, and rockpiles, edges, nest boxes or abandoned buildings, to name a few.

❏ Space: Every creature has its own needs for space or territory. What seems just right for a chickadee would be a tight squeeze for a moose.

Also consider these principles:

❏ Arrangement: Food, water and cover must be arranged in a way to be most accessible to the animal.

❏ Corridors: Wildlife needs continuous lanes of habitat through which to safely travel between areas that provide for different needs.

❏ Variety: The more kinds of plants the better for a wider range of wildlife. A variety of plants also means there will always be an adequate diversity, even if bugs or disease do kill some varieties.

❏ Carrying Capacity: There is a limit to how many animals of any one species can be sustained on an area of land over time, which is determined by the quantity and quality of habitat components.

❏ Limiting Factor: This is the need in shortest supply that prevents the wildlife population from getting any larger. To increase a population, determine what is holding it down, and correct for that.

❏ Plant Succession: The naturally occurring effects of plant succession can be used to attain desired habitat conditions.

❏ Habitat Types: Different schoolyards are comprised of different habitats. Expect to attract only those species for which your site can provide the necessary habitat.

❏ Native Plants and Seeds: The wildlife of your area is best adapted to native vegetation. These plants are best suited for your region and can survive with much less care than non-native plants.

❑   Buffers: Plant shrubs and trees between high activity areas and the wildlife areas so wildlife will be screened from people. Use plants with thick growth to act as natural fences.

❑   Change of Seasons: Food, water and cover must be available all year long. Plant a variety of plants that bloom and fruit at different times of the year. Provide both summer and winter protection with evergreen trees and shrubs.

❑   Climate: Plants that enjoy the climate of your area will last long after you've put them in the ground. Choose hardy species that will live for years.

❑   Soils: Healthy soils grow healthy plants. Information about testing and improving your site's soil is available from the Department of Agriculture or Soil Conservation Service (see Appendix G).

(Adapted with permission from Living with Wildlife Series, Unit 7, <u>Habitat in the Year 2000</u>, Canadian Wildlife Federation and Washington Department of Wildlife. <u>Urban Wildlife Series: Landscape Design for Wildlife</u>. Booklet)

Material for this chapter excerpted or adapted with permission from:

Living with Wildlife Series, Unit 7, *Habitat in the Year 2000*, Canadian Wildlife Federation

Environmental Awareness — Wildlife, Otis F. Curtis, University of Connecticut Cooperative Extension System

Elliott, C.A., 1988. *A Forester's Guide to Managing Wildlife Habitats in Maine*. University of Maine Cooperative Extension, Orono, ME 04469.

Henderson, Carrol L., 1987. *Landscaping for Wildlife*. MN Dept. of Nat. Res. St. Paul

Washington Department of Wildlife. *Urban Wildlife Series: Landscape Design for Wildlife*. Booklet 12 pp.

✍ **Activities from the Project WILD activity guide,** for learning about the wildlife concepts presented in Chapter 2.

Grades	Title	Concept(s)
K-1	Everybody Needs a Home	habitat needs
	Classroom Carrying Capacity	carrying capacity
2-3	Everybody Needs a Home	habitat needs
	Classroom Carrying Capacity	carrying capacity
	Beautiful Basics, The	wildlife habitat needs
	What's That, Habitat?	compare human/ wildlife habitat needs
	Habitracks	compare human/wildlife habitat needs
3-4	Beautiful Basics, The	wildlife habitat needs
	Ants on a Twig	wildlife habitat needs
	What's for Dinner?	plants as food
	How Many Bears Can Live in this Forest?	carrying capacity
	Classroom Carrying Capacity	carrying capacity
4-6	Beautiful Basics, The	wildlife habitat needs
	What's for Dinner?	plants as food
	How Many Bears Can Live in this Forest?	carrying capacity
	Classroom Carrying Capacity	carrying capacity
	Habitat Rummy	habitat needs
	Habitat Lap Sit	habitat components, habitat loss
	Oh, Deer!	carrying capacity
	Quick Frozen Critters	predator/prey, limiting factors
	Muskox Maneuvers	predator/prey, limiting factors
7-9	Beautiful Basics, The	wildlife habitat
	Habitat Lap Sit	habitat components
	How Many Bears Can Live in this Forest?	carrying capacity
	Oh, Deer!	carrying capacity
	Muskox Maneuvers	predator/prey, limiting factors

Section II
Taking Inventory

*"We seek contacts with nature because we
derive pleasure from them."*

Aldo Leopold, The Land Ethic

Chapter 3
Mapping the Schoolyard

A map of your schoolyard site allows you to view the inventory information in a single clear format, so you can make decisions concerning habitat enhancements.

A Picture is Worth a Thousand Words

In the context of planning your wildlife program, that old saying takes on increased meaning. The map is a critical piece of this project. It serves as the base on which to apply all your inventory data as you collect it. And it will be the standard that all members of your team refer to in doing their work.

Since some of the data you will gather influences the map making, part of the inventory process (discussed in Chapter 4) will need to be done prior to making your map. For instance, you will need to know overall size of the site, placement of buildings and other permanent structures, and location of vegetation.

As you will see in the following mapping guidelines, some of this information can be collected from published maps and other sources. You may choose to use these, and/or go out in your schoolyard and inventory features with your students.

Map-Making with Children

Some people feel uncomfortable with maps — unable to find the information they're seeking, or confused about foreign symbols. You may feel overwhelmed by maps. Your students may not have worked with them yet. The exercises at the end of this chapter will allow you and your students to become familiar with maps before you begin to map your site.

Steps Toward an Ecology of the Schoolyard

Your students can actively participate in mapping the schoolyard site. They can create picture maps, 3-D maps, and drawn maps. While their maps may not be to scale, they will demonstrate for you what features are significant to the students.

Students from every grade level can do some kind of mapping for this project. While the older students may produce the more technically accurate map you need for the site inventory, having all the students take part in mapping will develop their awareness of what is on the site and increase their observation and map-making skills.

You will find each grade level interprets land in map form in different ways. It is more important to allow students to create the map as they see it, rather than trying to get them all to do the same kind of map.

Provide a variety of maps for the students to study. Include aerial view maps (like road maps), maps with highlighted features (like scenic tour maps), maps with combined aerial and pictorial features (like trail guides), and pictoral maps (like city tourist maps).

Sample Mapping Sequence
Experiment with a mapping sequence, like the one outlined below, to allow your students to practice map-making.

1. Creating a Display Map:
Create a large map (perhaps 3' by 4' or larger) of the schoolyard. Include prominent features and boundaries in fairly accurate geographic proportions: the location of the school, nearby roads, streams, wetlands, etc. Try to include the essential human-made and natural infrastructures — not too much and not too little.

2. Creating Individual Working Maps
Make an 8" x 11" version of the display map so individual students and teachers can have their own copy. Use these individual copies for field work. Field work might include:

      checking the location of prominent features
      identifying locations of animal signs
      mapping paths of informal trails
      designing habitat enhancement projects

3. Elaborating the Display Map
Two possible separate stages. The first stage is using the students' observations to locate presently existing features on the map. Take various student ideas and make a group decision about where things should be on the map. The second stage is synthesizing the students' habitat enhancement projects and putting them all on the map.

4. Creating a 3-D Model
Can be added on to when projects are completed.

Many variations of this sequence are possible. The main idea is for you to provide a large and small outline map as parameters for the work, and then engage the children in locating the rest of the landscape features and in planning the habitat enhancement. It's the balance between your scaffolding of the activities and the students' involvement that will make it work.

Experiment with:

- mapping small, then larger, areas
- creating a composite map from children's individual maps
- treasure maps
- texture maps, using materials taken from the site that are glued or rubbed onto the map
- sound maps, mapping sounds peculiar to specific areas within a site (see Joseph Cornell's *Sharing the Joy of Nature* for a sound mapping activity)
- mapping literature, creating a map of a place or journey that is described in a story
- sandtable geography
- attaching real objects to an outline map, in the area to which each object is related

(Excerpted with permission from a Map-making Workshop Handout, David Sobel, Antioch/New England Graduate School)

MAP-MAKING FOR SCHOOLYARD ENHANCEMENT PROJECTS

Questions of Scale

When you are planning to draw a map, it is important to first establish a scale. By doing this, you determine a proportion between the size of objects on the map relative to actual objects on the ground. Maintain this proportion throughout the map surface.

The Base Map

Identify the area that you plan to enhance. It may be a small courtyard, a corner of the playground, or a larger area of fields, wetlands and woods.

This border outline of your site, called your "base map," will show only those things that are permanent or unlikely to change, such as boundaries and locations of structures. From the base map you will construct overlays from the information collected in your inventory (see Chapter 4).

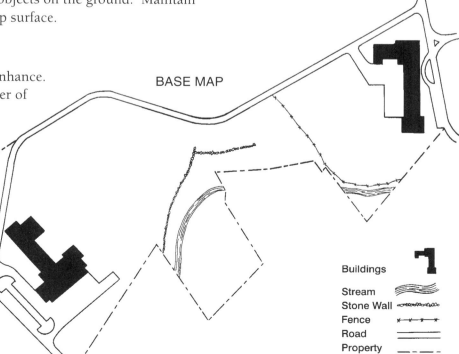

BASE MAP

Buildings

Stream

Stone Wall

Fence

Road

Property
Boundary

The base map includes:

- the boundaries of the property
- soil type in the area
- location of buildings and roads
- water bodies

You can sketch a simple border map of this area on site, or draw one from existing maps. Some of these, such as USGS topographic maps and aerial photographs, will require that you enlarge the scale; others you may be able to use directly, such as boundary surveys and site plans from when the school was built.

Sources of base maps:

- tax map for general boundary information
- site plot or plan from town office or county registry of deeds
- survey maps
- USGS (U.S. Geological Survey) topographic maps (requires enlargement of scale)
- aerial photos (helps with interpretation)
- Soil Conservation Service, County Soil and Water Conservation Districts, ASCS (Agricultural Stabilization and Conservation Service)

If you have a boundary survey map of your site, you have the battle half-won. These have accurate boundaries and locations of structures, are generally of a large enough scale for you to work from, and may contain topographic data as well.

Nevertheless, there is no substitute for your own in-depth familiarity with your site. Draw on your knowledge of the site, put it to scale, and render it into a map form that will allow you to accomplish your planning effort. Precision is fine, but keep in kind that the final product you are working toward is wildlife habitat enhancement and not a surveyor's license.

Map Symbols and Legend

There are many standard symbols used in map-making. Some of the most common ones are shown on the sample base map. You may create additional symbols to represent unique features on your site.

To represent common features, these standard colors are used:

black — human-made structures
red — roads
blue — water
green — forested areas
brown — contour lines

Your choice of colors may be more extensive and need not conform to standard symbols.

"We used mixed groups of 1st-6th graders to do the project – a very beneficial arrangement! First and second graders understand habitat, third and fourth graders grasped the project, and fifth and sixth graders provided data and information for group meetings."

NANCY SANDELL
PIERMONT SCHOOL
PIERMONT, NH

It is important to label all your map symbols so anyone looking at your map can understand it. The best way to make your map understandable is to provide a legend. A legend is simply a boxed-in area on your map page that delineates each symbol or color used and what each represents.

Making Map Overlays

Overlays are probably the most efficient means of transcribing a lot of information into map form. By using overlays you will protect your base map from becoming cluttered with too much information.

An overlay is simply a sheet of tracing paper or acetate laid over your base map, with the border outline drawn onto it. New details are added to the overlay. Place registration marks in opposite corners of the base map and each overlay to align them.

Each overlay contains a different type of infor: want at least three different overlays. One, co from your vegetation inventory, is called the " A second, containing soils information derive county soil survey, is called the "soils types m: The third, with division lines indicating differ management areas, is called the "wildlife management units map." You can create other overlays as needed.

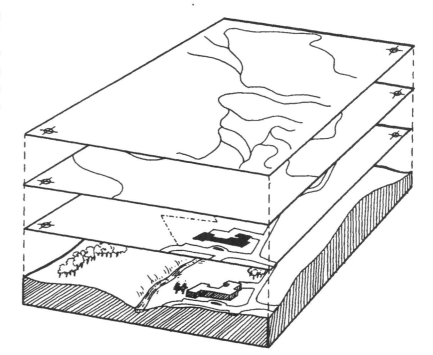

Making Overlay I: Cover Type Map

A cover type map is used to describe the types, structure, and arrangement of vegetative cover that you have on your site. This overlay will include the data from your site inventory concerning vegetation and water. The amount of detail you put into this map depends on what information you need for your planning efforts.

Vegetative cover types will appear on your map as patches on the terrain. To show them pictorially, designate a certain color for each cover type and color in the area on the map that coincides with each type as it exists on your site. For example, you may choose to represent lawn with light green, shrubs with medium green, and trees with dark green.

Types of vegetation: These are some general categories in which vegetation is placed to simplify assessment.

- Softwood forest: Dominated by needle-leaved trees and shrubs which hold their leaves year-round (evergreens).
- Hardwood forest: Dominated by broad-leaved trees and shrubs which shed their leaves each fall (deciduous).

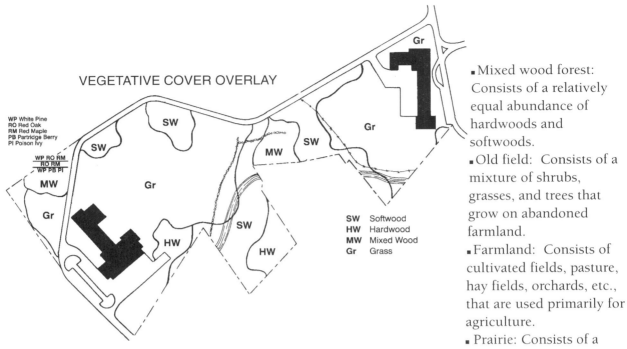

VEGETATIVE COVER OVERLAY

WP White Pine
RO Red Oak
RM Red Maple
PB Partridge Berry
PI Poison Ivy

WP RO RM
RO RM
WP PB PI

SW Softwood
HW Hardwood
MW Mixed Wood
Gr Grass

■Mixed wood forest: Consists of a relatively equal abundance of hardwoods and softwoods.

■Old field: Consists of a mixture of shrubs, grasses, and trees that grow on abandoned farmland.

■Farmland: Consists of cultivated fields, pasture, hay fields, orchards, etc., that are used primarily for agriculture.

■ Prairie: Consists of a variety of grasses and other herbaceous plants.

To add more detail to your map, you can describe the three most abundant plant species in each layer of vegetation: overstory, midstory, and ground cover. This is usually done by developing a coding system for the plants and placing the codes into a three-tier configuration in the colored cover type area where they were found.

In addition, indicate any special features of vegetation such as standing dead trees and trees with woodpecker cavities or natural holes. Assign each a symbol or code and locate them on the cover type map.

Water — streams, springs, seeps, and ponds — should have a color code (usually blue) and be located on the cover type map as well as on the base map. If necessary, this information can also be included on the other overlays. From all this information you will have a good picture of your site's cover and water resources.

The cover type map is now ready for you to use as a tool in developing the habitat enhancement plan.

Making Overlay II: Soils Type Map
Soil types and conditions determine the species of vegetation that will thrive on your site, and how they need to be managed. The best source for soils information is your county soil survey. Copies can usually be obtained from your county Soil Conservation Service office or county extension office.

You will find that the surveys contain maps of relatively large areas. Locate your site within one of the map pages and enlarge the soils boundaries to fit your base map scale. Precision is not critical here since the accuracy of the soils maps is somewhat limited. Nevertheless, they can be useful in a general sense.

You also will find descriptions of the soils and their suitability and productivity for different land uses. Reading the soil survey book will provide valuable background information that may be useful as well.

Making Overlay III: Management Plan Map

This map organizes your site into different management projects or areas. It allows you more flexibility when applying enhancement activities. Dividing your site into units generally follows a particular pattern that reflects the primary purpose for enhancement activities.

Often the boundaries of individual units coincide with the boundaries of different habitat types. The number of units that you designate will depend on your interests, site size, and the diversity of resources available.

Geographic Information Systems (GIS) Maps

GIS maps may be helpful in the preparation of your site maps. They are computer-based surveys of a range of features, including surface waters, town boundaries, groundwater, geology and soils, prepared on a standard scale of 1:24,000.

This survey information is available in both digital data and printed map form, usually for a fee. Contact your state university, Soil Conservation Service, or state department of natural resources for information on what areas of your state have been mapped and how to access the data.

Checkpoint:

1) Have your maps reviewed by a professional, such as a county extension agent/educator or forester, to be sure you are on the right track.

2) Have people who are not involved with the project try to read and use your maps.

Remember, these maps will become the basis for your habitat enhancement record. If done well, they will allow future team members to better understand what the site looked like at the start of the process, what you have completed to date, and what your plans are for further enhancement efforts.

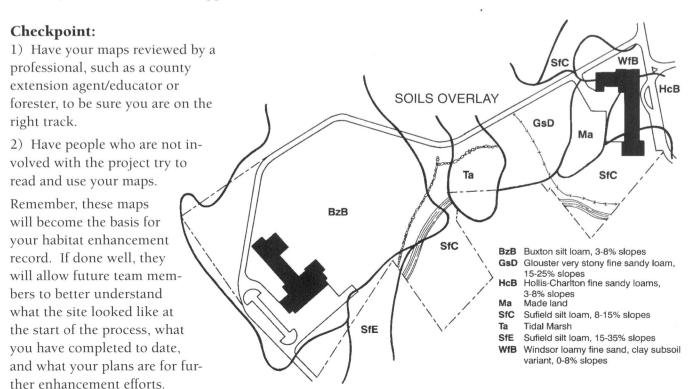

SOILS OVERLAY

SfC
WfB
HcB
GsD
Ma
Ta
SfC
BzB
SfC
SfE

BzB Buxton silt loam, 3-8% slopes
GsD Glouster very stony fine sandy loam, 15-25% slopes
HcB Hollis-Charlton fine sandy loams, 3-8% slopes
Ma Made land
SfC Sufield silt loam, 8-15% slopes
Ta Tidal Marsh
SfE Sufield silt loam, 15-35% slopes
WfB Windsor loamy fine sand, clay subsoil variant, 0-8% slopes

✍ MAP PRACTICE ACTIVITIES

Learning to Read and Use Maps

Collect several samples of maps: road maps, gazetteers, topographical maps, geological survey maps, etc. Post them in the classroom and have your students look at each one. Then complete the following:

1. Each map has a unique combination of physical and cultural features. Physical features, like rivers and mountains, are part of the land itself or shaped by land forms. Cultural features are things built or made by people, like towns and roads. Find examples of both.

2. Look at the maps to find examples of the following features: mountain, lake, railroad, road, scenic site. What towns are they near? Choose an example of each feature from different maps, and draw a picture of them.

3. Find a place name that is related to a local physical feature. For example, Portsmouth is a port town located at the mouth of a river.

4. Look at the legend on the map. This is a list of the symbols used on the map, with an explanation of what each means. Some symbols are standard and found on nearly every map; others are unique to individual maps or map types. Usually the legend appears in the bottom corner of the map.

5. If you were a cartographer or map maker and needed a symbol to represent a town, what would you draw? Remember to make it recognizable to other people.

6. Copy the legend symbols from several maps, excluding the explanation. Then have your students try to figure out what each symbol represents.

Practice working with different kinds of maps in this way until you and your students are comfortable and familiar with maps and what they mean. Having the students make their own maps will help them learn how to translate information into a map.

Using Thinking Skills to Study Maps

Map-making is the perfect integrated curriculum project. It is impossible to do it well without straying into all major curriculum realms. By studying maps, students learn to use critical thinking and problem solving skills (as noted in parentheses following each activity below).

Explore the following as map-related activities:

1. What is a map? Develop and apply several definitions to different maps. Check your definition with the dictionary. Is a globe a map? (definition)

2. Examine a map. How are lines used in different ways to represent rivers, roads, borders, and boundaries between land and water? (analysis)

3. Examine a variety of maps. Identify the features these maps have in common. Discuss why maps have these features. (attributions)

4. Why are some of the borders of countries straight lines while others are curvy? (inferences)

5. What is the relationship between one mile on a map and a real mile? (relationships)

6. How can you measure the real distance of a curvy river like the Mississippi? (brainstorming)

7. Find two cities on a map that look about 200 miles apart. Find two more that also look about 200 miles apart. Check your estimates. (estimation)

8. How are the lines on a contour map like those on a rainfall map? On a weather map? Where else do you find these kinds of lines? (associations)

9. What are some of the effects of projecting a curved surface, like the earth, onto a flat surface, like a map? Cite some examples, using globes and maps. (casual reasoning)

10. Draw a map from an aerial photograph. Trace it or draw it free-hand. How did you decide what to include and what to omit? (simplification)

11. Look at the *Times Atlas of World History* (Hammond, Inc.), which uses unconventional views of many sites of historic importance. Discuss how these views better illustrate the significance of historic places. (point of view)

12. Draw a map, from the picture in your mind, of how you walk from home to school. What landmarks help you? Are some details much bigger or smaller than they should be? Why? (imaging)

13. On a map, draw all the ways to get home from school. This is a network. Now draw five cities on a piece of paper. Link the five cities by roads. Each city must be linked directly to every other one without passing through another city. What is the least number of roads? (networking)

14. Using several points of origin and destinations, predict the quickest way to get from one point to another. Follow up by testing your predictions. Where were your predictions off? Why? (prediction)

15. Show the pattern of litter on the school playground. How do you best represent the playground, its features, the litter? Do all areas have the same amount of litter? Do some have more? Less? Why is the litter distributed like this? Make up a plan to test your hunch. (graphic representation)

16. Complete analogies about maps.

    A map is to a _____ as _____ is to a _____.

    A map is like a _____.

    A map is like a shoe because_____.

    (analogies)

(Excerpted with permission from <u>CONNECT</u> *Math and Science Newsletter, May 1989 issue, Teacher's Laboratory, Inc.)*

Material for this chapter excerpted or adapted with permission from:

"Using Thinking Skills to Study Maps," <u>CONNECT</u>, Math and Science Newsletter, May 1989, Teacher's Laboratory, Inc.

Wildlife Habitat Improvement Series. David Langley, University of New Hampshire Cooperative Extension, 1993.

Map-making Workshop Handout, David Sobel, Antioch/New England Graduate School, Keene, NH

Chapter 4

Conducting the Site Inventory

As the next step in the planning process, you will want to find out in some detail what is on your site. With your base map completed, you can now begin a site inventory.

TAKING INVENTORY

Why Survey?

Site surveying is in itself a valuable teaching exercise, suitable for all ages of students if approached in an appropriate manner. From this they may learn not only simple surveying techniques, practical math and basic plan making, but are introduced to the concept of the interdependence of humans with their physical and social environment.

Site surveying also provides the basis for the enhancement plan:

1) as a drawing on which the plan is superimposed, and

2) as a source of information and inspiration by identifying the following:

- the space available for enhancement
- characteristics of the site; for example, its potential to be utilized and its problems to be overcome
- existing features to be retained.

Awareness of Your Site

Begin with a list. Have the students list all the things they notice or know about the property before you begin a formal survey. One way to do this is to become part of the site. (Refer to Chapter 1 for activities that build connections with the site.)

MAKING ROOM FOR WILDLIFE

The following piece, while written for landowners, will apply to your school site enhancement efforts.

"Creating a natural harmony on your property begins with a plan that is based on an awareness of the wildlife potential of your land. Part of this whole process involves being in touch with your surroundings. This process begins in the morning. Wake up early before the dawn and sit outside your home as the sun begins to rise. Listen for the sounds of a new day and see what life is waking up around you. Hear the chirps of songbirds, and then see which birds are making their early morning calls. Listen for the chatter of squirrels, or alarm sounds of the chipmunk. Walk the woods or fields on your lands and look for the signs of nocturnal animals. Are there any tracks to be seen? Did a deer, raccoon, or opossum come through while it was dark?

"Follow the sun as the day progresses and map its path across the sky. Learn which parts of your land receive the most sunlight, and discover those areas that remain shaded throughout the day. How will the land be affected as the seasons progress during the year? Monitor the local populations of birds as they pass through, noticing which ones stay, and which ones keep going. What animals are missing that you would like to see? Why are they not there? Knowing the answers to these questions during each season of the year is a key to being in touch with the Earth and the land that you live on, and live with. The discovery of the life that is found all around you aids in the development of a wildlife management plan for yor land."

Excepted with permission from "Making Room for Wildlife on a Small Scale" by Randall Shank, <u>Virginia Wildlife</u>, November 1988.

INVENTORY TOOLS

Here are some tools to collect in preparation for your inventory:
    base map(s) of the site
    tape measures
    clipboards
    paper
    pencils
    string
    collecting containers
    thermometers
    field guides and keys

Practical Inventory Process

The complexity of this process will be determined by both the size of the land area you plan to enhance, and the types of projects you may already have in mind. You can share the work with the team. Assign smaller groups or individuals to inventory and map specific features on the site. Or have the teachers divide the list of features, then each complete a portion of the inventory with their students.

Components of the Site Inventory

A good site inventory will include features from three areas:

1. Physical (rocks, outcrops, trees, plants, landmarks)
2. Wildlife (signs and sightings)
3. Human (educational, utilitarian, and socio-cultural)

It can also include some personal reflections on the site, such as aesthetic appreciation in poetry or prose, or remarks on historical influences. Include notes on the areas surrounding your schoolyard.

On Surrounding Areas

Wildlife habitats are rarely confined by distinct borders, such as the parameters of a schoolyard. Just as we may travel into other towns or states to shop for food or clothing, so wildlife species which utilize your site to meet some of their needs are probably satisfying other needs in surrounding areas.

Because of this, it is important to map and consider the surrounding community. Its composition can have a significant effect on certain wildlife species that might be attracted to your site. For example, though your site includes a grassy field that would provide food for deer, if the surrounding community is a paved downtown area that offers no forest cover, it is unlikely that deer will be found there.

Consider the whole schoolyard and surrounding areas as the complete habitat. Most wildlife species require a range of space that extends beyond your site; many may find some elements of their habitat on your site, and meet other requirements in surrounding areas. The birds that eat at your feeders, for example, may be nesting in a nearby woodlot. The deer you've attracted to your pond for watering may be eating the corn in a nearby field.

Safety Precautions in the Field

As you prepare to take your students into the schoolyard to conduct an inventory, consider the following safety precautions.

Different habitats require different clothing. If wandering in mowed, cleared areas, students should wear closed-toed shoes (preferably sneakers) and socks that are pulled up. Hats, caps and shirts with sleeves will protect skin from the sun. If students are working in wooded areas or abandoned fields, they should also wear long pants and long socks (with socks pulled up over pant legs) and, in some seasons, insect repellent. Deer and dog ticks will occur in grassy areas; check exposed areas of the skin when returning from being outdoors.

Most schoolyard organisms can be examined and handled with no harm or, at most, scratches from thorns or bites from grasshoppers. Teach your students that careless handling can injure the plant or animal as well as the student.

Caution students to avoid dense underbrush and not to reach into holes. Warn them not to eat any schoolyard plants and animals. Although most brightly colored fruits are harmless (some leave a bad taste in your mouth), others can be poisonous. Some mushrooms can be deadly poisonous; students should be warned never to eat a wild mushroom of any variety, even when a self-professed expert on edible wild mushrooms is present. As a precaution, students should wash their hands after handling mushrooms. In fact, it is a good idea for students to wash their hands immediately after any schoolyard activity.

The hairs on many local caterpillars irritate the skin or even give a sharp sting, as do the hairs on at least one common plant (stinging nettle). The damage potential of some organisms (bees, wasps, poison ivy) is well known, but do not assume that all your pupils share in that knowledge. Poison ivy occurs frequently. A bee sting kit may be a wise addition to your school's first aid package. Teachers should already be aware of any children who have allergies to insect stings or certain pollens.

Contact with live or dead mammals should be avoided, as some carry disease that can infect humans. (Permits are required to collect certain wildlife specimens; check with your state wildlife agency.) Bites and scratches from wild mammals are potentially serious and should receive professional medical attention. For example, raccoons, who have adapted to life in human communities and do not usually fear humans, can carry diseases such as distemper and rabies.

A final caution. For the sake of plants and animals you investigate, please be ethical in your treatment of the wild creatures that share your school grounds. If you move animals to another site for observation, return them to the place of capture when you are done. Any logs, boards or rocks that are turned over in the course of your investigations should be returned to their original positions.

(Adapted with permission from the Handbook to Schoolyard Plants and Animals of North Central Florida, Peter Fensinger and Maria Minno, Florida Game and Fresh Water Fish Commission.)

Adapt this list to the needs of your project.

Site Inventory Outline

Following is an outline of specific features to inventory in preparation for drafting your enhancement plan. Adapt this list to the needs of your project, using those elements that apply to your particular site.

I. Information to inventory for each feature
   a. What it is
   b. Type and kind
   c. Size
   d. Location
   e. Number

II. Physical Characteristics
   A. Natural Features
      1. Topography - high and low sites
         a. Landforms, acreage, major slope areas, approximate degree of slope
      2. Surface geology
         a. Bedrock exposures, glacial deposits, sand banks, etc.
      3. Soil conditions
         a. Color, consistency, porosity, composition, acidity, nutrients
      4. Surface water
         a. Sources and dimensions: lakes, ponds, streams, swamps, marshes, bogs
      5. Environmental conditions
         a. Temperature, high and low
         b. Exposure: prevailing wind, summer and winter
         c. Weather
         d. Rainfall, humidity
         e. Sources of noise
         f. Sunny and shaded areas
   B. Human-related (some of these may already appear on your base map)
      1. Containment features: fences, walls, etc.
      2. Habitation features: buildings, etc.
      3. Transportation/mobility features: walkways, established trails, roads, parking lots, bus stops, etc.
      4. Utility features: maintenance facilities, waste disposal areas, power plants, utility lines, etc.
      5. Activity features: playground structures, ball fields, outdoor meeting areas, etc.

III. Biological Characteristics - Terrestrial and Aquatic

  A. Flora (vegetation), native and exotic
    1. Dominant and other notable species
      a. Shrubs
      b. Grasses
      c. Trees
      d. Garden areas, landscaped areas
    2. Plant Communities
      a. Playing fields and grassy openings
      b. Wooded areas
      c. Wetland areas
  B. Fauna (wildlife), native and exotic
    1. Wildlife currently using property
      a. Species observed on site
      b. Species with recognizable signs
        1) Tracks
        2) Scat (droppings)
        3) Partially consumed food
    2. Insects
    3. Birds
    4. Mammals
    5. Reptiles and Amphibia
    6. Wildlife habitat features
      a. Burrows
      b. Tree cavities
      c. Dead or partly dead trees (snags)
      d. Nesting areas
      e. Perching areas
      f. Drinking and feeding areas
      g. Refuge areas
      h. Travel corridors
      i. Existing bird feeders, bird baths, bird houses
      j. Hazards to wildlife

IV. Socio-Cultural Characteristics — Historic and Current

  A. Human land use history
    1. Current use
    2. Service and protective utilities
    3. Overhead and underground utilities
    4. Safety hazards
    5. Examples of environmental degradation or abuse
  B. Adjacent conditions
    1. General characteristics of the surrounding area
      a. Neighboring trees, buildings, roadways

"Invite the elderly and retired community members into your classroom. They have a great historical perspective of the changes habitats have gone through. Students also seem to have a natural respect and rapport with the elderly."

BIANCA MCRAE
RAYMOND SCHOOL
RAYMOND, NH

V. Characteristics for Objective Comment
   A. Special features
       1. Most prominent feature
       2. Most unique feature
       3. Historical features
       4. Features to protect or preserve
   B. Recreational considerations
   C. Educational values
   D. Economic values
   E. Personal reflections
   F. Things to look for that may support environmental interpretation
       1. Unusual/unique features
       2. Features of historical significance
       3. Wildlife habitats and vegetative communities
       4. Evidence of survival adaptations
       5. Evidence of natural or ecological processes: succession, reproduction, decomposition, cycles, interrelationships
       6. Evidence of changes (desirable and undesirable)
       7. Renewable, non-renewable, and recyclable resources
       8. Features of school's "life support" system: energy/power resources, water supply, waste disposal/treatment, safety, communications

Site Inventory – Activity Cards
Use the activity cards, located at the end of this chapter, to develop an initial concept of the diverse composition of features on your schoolyard site. While some of these activities may not appear to relate to wildlife and wildlife habitat, it is always valuable to get an overall concept of features on a schoolyard site when taking on a project like this. Sometimes, the resulting data may be less significant than what your students note in the process.

USING KEYS

It is helpful to know how to use a key when you're doing a site inventory. This will allow you to separate out and identify different species of plants and animals. The best way to gain understanding of a key is to construct one.

Learning the Use of Keys
The objective of the following technique is to help your students become independent and persistent in their search for the correct name. This is a

"The fifth graders researched specific trees using field guides and keys, learned about their trees and drew the habitats before doing the plantings."

MATT FERGUSON
DEERFIELD COMMUNITY SCHOOL
DEERFIELD, NH

case where directing their experience can be helpful. The first attempt might be a class effort with your assistance.

Method:
Assemble a small collection of common objects, for example, fruit.

Discuss ways in which these fruits differ. These differences (shape, texture, color, taste, size, etc.) will provide clues leading to their names.

Start by making a pair of statements (Clue 1) about one of the differences. Group the fruits in accordance with these.

Clue 1:
    Round – apple, orange, tomato. Move to clue 2.
    Not round – pear, lemon, banana. Move to clue 4.

    Deal with the round things first. Make another pair of statements for the second clue.

Clue 2:
    Skin rather tasteless – apple, tomato. Move to clue 3.
    Skin bitter tasting – orange.

    Since an orange is the only fruit fitting this clue it is not necessary to go any further.

    Make the next clue to separate the apple and tomato.

Clue 3:
    Soft, easily squashed – tomato.
    Hard, not easily squashed – apple.

    Now return to the group of fruits that were not round.

Clue 4:
    Less than 6 inches in length – pear, lemon. Move to clue 5.
    More than 6 inches in length – banana.

    Make the final clue to separate the pear and lemon.

Clue 5:

Skin thick - lemon

Skin not thick - pear.

This way of separating the fruits could be recorded in the following way.

Now it is easy to see that the original set has been subdivided into smaller and smaller sub-sets on the basis of fruits possessing or lacking a character, or of being opposite to each other in certain ways.

(Adapted from Using the Environment: 4 Ways and Means, *MacDonald Educational, Milwaukee)*

OTHER INVENTORY TECHNIQUES

The String Grid Method

1) On your schoolyard site, assemble a 1-meter-square grid, subdivided by lengths of string into 100 squares measuring 10x10 centimeters.

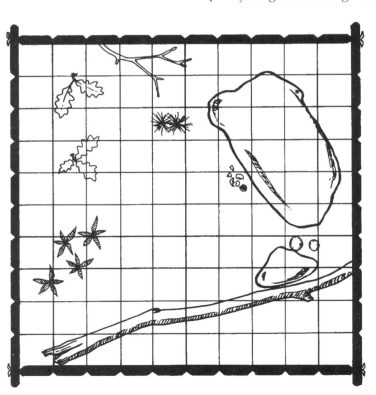

2) Working four in a group, hold the lengths of dowel rod in the positions shown in the diagram with the connecting strings taut. Push the ends of the two longer lengths of dowelling between the Terry clips.

3) Place the grid over a pool or small area.

4) Select a suitable scale and plot the outline of the study area, and details of its contents, onto a squared paper.

When the grid is taken apart, the strings of each section should be rolled on to one of the lengths of dowelling to prevent tangling during transport and storage.

(Excerpted from Trees, *MacDonald Educational, Milwaukee)*

The Baseline and Offset Method

1) Use a long rope knotted at 1-yard intervals. By means of metal meat skewers fixed to each end of this rope, peg it to the ground alongside or across the site to be mapped, whichever is more convenient.

2) Then peg out another rope at right angles to the baseline from the first knot to the far boundary of the site. This line is an offset. Offsets should similarly be made from the other knots. A blackboard set square of a piece of paper folded in four can be used to check right angles between baseline and offsets.

3) Use squared paper and select a convenient scale and draw a line to represent the baseline. Using the same scale, plot the two points of inter-section between each offset and the boundary of the site. By joining neighboring points an outline for the site can then be obtained.

As students become more experienced they may find that fewer offsets can give sufficient data for satisfactory outlines of some sites to be drawn. The position of prominent landmarks on the site can also be fixed by taking offsets from the baseline to them.

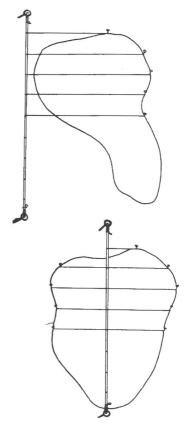

Collecting and Recording Information with a Grid System

1) Start at one corner of your site. Walk a straight line along the edge of the site, stopping every 50 yards to record habitat information. Record only what is within a 25 yard radius of each stopping point to prevent double entries.

2) When you reach the opposite boundary, move over 50 yards and walk a straight line parallel to the first line, stopping and record-ing every 50 yards, until you reach the origi-nal boundary from which you started.

3) Repeat the procedure of moving over 50 yards and walking parallel lines, stopping and recording every 50 yards, until you have covered your entire site. This may take several days to complete, depending on the size of your site.

You may wish to use a hand-held compass to ensure you are walking parallel lines. You can determine how many paces you walk in fifty yards so you won't have to carry a tape measure.

(Excerpted with permission from Wildlife Habitat Improvement Series, David Langley, University of New Hampshire Cooperative Extension, 1993)

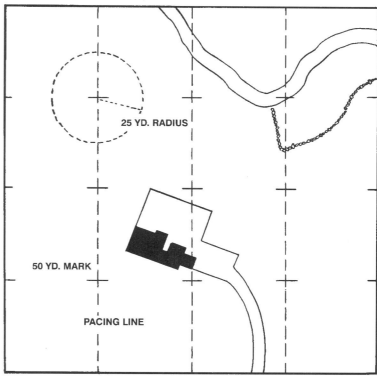

25 YD. RADIUS

50 YD. MARK

PACING LINE

"Students can do a site inventory and keep the information in a journal over time. A master log is a plan for the future, kept in the library."

MATT FERGUSON
DEERFIELD COMMUNITY SCHOOL
DEERFIELD, NH

Keeping Records

Regardless of what activities you choose, keep a record of everything you do. Don't wait until you're finished with an activity before you sit down and write about it. A good field ecologist (a wildlife student like yourself is a field ecologist) always records observations as they are made.

If you don't have good records, you'll wish you did, so start your notations when you start your project. Your records needn't be complicated; think of them as a scientific diary. Make them clear, concise, and to the point, and they will be useful later.

Document expenses and actions, on paper and with photography. By taking pictures of your site from exactly the same location every year you can dramatically document the success of your habitat project and share it with others.

ASSESS YOUR FINDINGS

Now look at the information you have collected about your site, and begin to set your objectives by answering the following questions:

1. What kind of soil type, sunlight, and climate conditions must plants be able to tolerate to thrive on this site?

2. Which areas of the site are best-suited for school uses and needs? How should these areas be modified to make them more suitable or comfortable? Do they need screening or protection from sun, wind, or traffic?

3. Are there any areas of the schoolyard property that are not used for any activity, and could be replaced with wildlife habitat plantings?

4. What existing features can become a starting point for enhancing wildlife habitat? Examples might include:

   - an existing stand of native vegetation
   - large, old shade trees
   - scattered trees and shrubs that could be connected into one large planting
   - presence of water - stream, pond, canal, spring, wetland
   - presence of wildlife species
   - topographic variety

5. Identify resources in short supply relative to food, cover, and water for wildlife (develop a list).

With your inventory data and map in hand, you can now identify those plant and animal species your site supports, or could potentially support. Recall the four components of habitat: food, water, shelter, and space. What combinations of these components does your site provide? How do you meet the needs of wildlife species? Refer to several field guides and other reference books for information that will help you analyze your site as wildlife habitat.

For example, you may discover in this process that you have the space, water, and enough low-growing evergreen cover to support a few snowshoe hare, which you've learned are native to your area. If you plan to include hare in your enhancement project, you will need to consider whether you can improve food sources to complete the habitat components hare need.

It is valuable to recall, at this point, that space is the habitat component we can least influence.

What do You Want?

The working team can now brainstorm a list of desired species. Include those currently utilizing the property, as well as those you would like to attract. Think in terms of improving the overall habitat to benefit several species, rather than managing for a single species. (Look in Appendix C for habitat descriptions and associated wildlife species.)

Check each species on the list against the results of your site inventory. Note interrelationships among species, perhaps animals that function as predator and prey, or vegetation that provides animals with shelter, food, or other nutrients. Plan to provide all the necessary habitat components.

Review the vegetative and structural components needed for good wildlife habitat. Which are already present, which should be removed, which should be enhanced or added? Most schoolyards are not large and diverse enough to include all habitat components.

Check Point:

Before you and your students begin to invest energy and labor in habitat enhancement projects, confer with resource professionals and check reference materials to confirm your findings.

"When I had kids inventory trees on their plots, I had them divide the trees into size classifications using their hands and arms. They sized them as: plants you could put one hand around, 2 hands, 4 hands (you need a partner), 2 arms, and 4 arms. It was quick and easy and needed no equipment."
EMILY WRUBEL
HILLSBORO-DEERING SCHOOL
HILLSBORO, NH

A NOTE ON OBSERVING WILDLIFE

Observing wildlife is more than just looking at animals. Observing means perceiving, noticing, or watching. You are observing wildlife when you use your ears or nose to determine something about an animal and, strictly speaking, you are observing wildlife when you perceive by interpreting animal sign.

Practice and experience will make you a more skillful observer, just as practice and experience make you better at basketball or playing the piano. *Environmental Awareness - Wildlife* by Otis F. Curtis contains suggestions to make your wildlife observations more successful.

(See Appendix H for a listing of instructional resources.)

✍ SITE INVENTORY ACTIVITY CARDS

Developed by Jerry Schierloh, Associate Professor of Environmental Studies, New Jersey School of Conservation, for Graduate Course "Outdoor Teaching Sites for Environmental Education," Montclair State College.

Note: These cards have been formatted for photocopying.

PHYSICAL FEATURES

SIZE OF SCHOOLYARD SITE

Materials:
paper/pencil, tape measure

Procedure:
1. Use the measuring tape to estimate the average length of your walking step or pace.

2. Using your walking step or pace as a measuring tool, estimate the overall size of your schoolyard site, including buildings, (length x width = area, expressed in square feet or square meters).

3. Convert your measurements into acres (1 acre = 43,560 square feet or 4047 square meters).

4. Find out the enrollment of your school.

5. Figure out how many students there are per acre of land. Number of students divided by number acres = number students per acre.

6. Include your measurements on the sketch map.

HIGH/LOW TEMPERATURES

Materials:
4 thermometers (2 big, 2 small), paper/pencil

Procedure:

1. Find the two sites on the schoolyard site that represent the coldest and warmest air temperatures (4 ft. above ground level).

   coldest: _____ warmest: _____

2. What might be affecting these temperature recordings (for example, in shade, in sun, next to building or stream)?

3. Based on this data and what you already may know of the schoolyard site, decide on those areas of the schoolgrounds you would avoid exposing people to during the dead of winter and/or the heat of summer.

4. Indicate the location of these temperatures sites on the sketch map.

SURFACE ROCKS

Materials:
2 buckets, paper/pencil

Procedure:

Use the buckets to collect small samples of 6 of the most distinctive surface rocks you can find on the schoolyard site.

(Each rock in the collection must vary significantly from the other five in some distinctive way, other than size).

2. Based on each rock's appearance, try to determine something of its origin (i.e., what it's made up of, how it got there, and why it might be important there).

WET AND DRY SPOTS

Materials:
paper/pencil

Procedure:
1. Using your own criteria to decide "what's wet" and "what's dry", locate the wettest and driest spots on your schoolyard site (which are no closer than 25 ft. to a building).
2. Indicate the position of these two spots on the sketch map.
3. Be prepared to describe the nature of these two spots.
4. How does the nature of these areas relate to their past or current use by humans?

COVERED AREAS OF SCHOOLYARD SITE

Materials:
tape measure, paper/pencil

Procedure:
1. Use the measuring tape to estimate the average length of your walking step or pace.
2. By using your walking step/pace as a measuring tool, roughly estimate the combined total area of your schoolyard site which is covered by buildings and pavement. (length x width = area, expressed as square feet or square meters)
3. Convert the final answer to acreage using the following conversion factor: 1 acre = 43,560 square feet or 4047 square meters.
4. Find out the total acreage of the schoolyard site. Compute the percentage of your total schoolground acreage that is covered with buildings and pavement.
5. Indicate your various measurements on the sketch map.

BIOTIC FEATURES

ANIMAL SIGNS

Materials:
bucket, animal tracks book, plastic bags, paper/pencil

Procedure:

1. Locate as many different animal "signs" as you can on the overall schoolyard site.

   ("Sign" can mean anything you observe or otherwise sense that suggests the past or present occurrence of animals on the site, such as: actual sighting, sounds or calls, burrows, dens, nests, partially-consumed food, carcasses, tracks, feathers, fur, dropping, etc. The term "animal" can mean anything from an insect to a mammal.)

2. Whenever possible, name or speculate on the name of the animal that you think goes with each sign. Draw a sketch of at least 2 signs.

3. On the sketch map, indicate the approximate location of each sign discovered.

4. What animal seems to be most abundant on the schoolyard site? Which leaves the most visible evidence?

EARTHWORM ANALYSIS

Materials:
4 1-foot rulers, paper/pencil

Procedure:

1. On one of the school's grass-covered playfields, look for earthworm "castings" (little lumpy mounds of earth usually clumped around tiny burrow openings).

2. Randomly select several areas to study. Use the rulers to estimate the number of castings per square foot or square meter in each area.

3. Average these numbers from the various areas first. Then, based on this average, project the probable total surface castings per acre of field (using the figure 43,560 square feet/acre or 4047 square meters/acre).

4. What does this number of earthworm castings suggest is occurring in this field? Is this occurrence good or bad? Why?

AGENTS OF DECOMPOSITION

Materials:
paper/pencil

Procedure:
1. Make a survey of the site for "agents of decomposition" — things which can break "big things" into "little things" which can then be used to renew the growth of some life form (for example, mushrooms).

2. List these agents or evidence of their presence, and mark their approximate locations on the map.

MOST COMMON PLANTS

Materials:
tree, shrub and herb books; bucket for samples; paper/pencil

Procedure:
1. Find what appears to you to be the most common tree, the most common shrub and the most common herb (non-grass or turf) of the entire schoolyard site. Use the following definitions as guidelines:

   - Tree: erect, woody plant, typically with singular trunk, usually growing to large size (10-12 ft. high or above).
   - Shrub: woody plant, erect or non-erect (i.e. sprawling, trailing, or vine-like), typically multi-trunked (i.e. with more than a single stem coming out of the ground), usually smaller than tree stature.
   - Herb: Ground plants with fleshy tissue (non-woody).

2. Bring back a small sample (leaf, twig, flower, fruit, etc.) of each. (Note: be sure you can accurately identify and avoid poisonous plants, such as poison ivy, poison oak, or poison sumac.)

3. Use field guides or other references to determine names of the three most common plants you find.

Animal Foods (berries)

Materials:
fruit key, animal foods book, paper/pencil

Procedure:
1. Survey the schoolyard site for the variety of fruits and berries it contains.
2. Collect a small sample of the fruits (and also a small portion of the associated twig or branch, with leaves) to bring back for species verification.
3. Indicate the location of these animal foods on the sketch map.
4. Use field guides or other references to determine which native wildlife species in this area might benefit from the berry-producing plants you located.

Survival Adaptations

Materials:
paper bag, paper/pencil

Procedure:
1. Make a collection of different seeds found on the schoolyard site.
2. Categorize the seeds collected according to the dispersal methods their host plant has adopted (i.e. wind, gravity, attachment to "passers-by", etc.).
3. What other life-forms have developed special adaptations for survival on the site?

CULTURAL FEATURES

PROTECTIVE DEVICES

Materials:
paper/pencil

Procedure:
1. Survey the entire schoolyard site for features or devices that were designed and installed to protect the health and safety of human lives.

2. Indicate the approximate location of each protective feature on the sketch map.

SERVICE UTILITIES

Materials:
paper/pencil

Procedure:
1. On your schoolyard site, locate visible evidence of as many different kinds of human-serving utilities as you can (i.e., electricity, water, sewage lines, fuel oil).

2. Indicate on your sketch map where the visible portions of such utilities occur.

3. Of all the utilities noted, which do you think uses the most energy each year in serving the life-support system of the school? The least energy?

   (Note: This information may also be obtained from local utility companies.)

DATES WITH HISTORY

Materials:
Paper/pencil

Procedure:

1. Look for anything on the schoolyard site that is dated, such as a cornerstone on the school building, commemorative plaque, telephone pole.

2. Show the location of these dated objects or features on the map.

3. Record the dates. List the dated objects or features in chronological order, to tell a story or history of this immediate area.

4. Fill in the gaps of this story with any information you may personally know about the area.

OBJECTIVE ASPECTS

See Chapter 1 for the following activities:

> **25 Words**
> **An On-the-Spot Story**
> **Colors/Hues**

✍ **Activities from the Project WILD activity guide** to supplement the assessment and inventory process presented in Chapter 4.

Concepts discussed in these activities - "wildlife is all sizes," "wildlife is everywhere," "humans and wildlife share environments."

Grades	Title	Concept(s)
K-1	Wildlife is Everywhere!	search for evidence of wildlife
2-3	Wildlife is Everywhere!	search for evidence of wildlife
	Graphananimal	tally animals in two different, simulated environments
	Grasshopper Gravity	observe, handle, describe live grasshoppers
3-4	Wildlife is Everywhere!	search for evidence of wildlife
	Graphananimal	tally animals in two different, simulated environments
	Grasshopper Gravity	observe, handle, describe live grasshoppers
	Environmental Barometers	observe/count wildlife as indicators of environmental quality
4-6	Graphananimal	tally animals in two different, simulated environments
	Tracks!	plaster casts of animal tracks
	Interview a Spider	use interview techniques to research and write about wildlife
	Urban Nature Search	questionnaire to collect data
	Grasshopper Gravity	observe, handle, describe live grasshoppers
	Environmental Barometers	observe/count wildlife as indicators of environmental quality
	Microtrek Scavenger Hunt	wildlife sign scavenger hunt
7-9	Urban Nature Search	questionnaire to collect data
	Interview a Spider	use interview techniques to research and write about wildlife
	Grasshopper Gravity	observe, handle, describe live grasshoppers
	Microtrek Scavenger Hunt	wildlife sign scavenger hunt

Material for this chapter excerpted or adapted with permission from:

Environmental Awareness: Wildlife, Otis F. Curtis.
University of Connecticut, Cooperative Extension System.

Using the Environment: 4 Ways and Means.
MacDonald Educational, Milwaukee

Jerry Schierloh, Assoc. Professor of Environmental Studies
NJ School of Conservation, Documents from Graduate Course:
"Outdoor Teaching Sites for Environmental Education"
Montclair State College

Washington Department of Wildlife.
How to Create Your Own Backyard Wildlife Habitat as Seen at Lake Hill's Greenbelt Ranger Station. Pamphlet

WILD School Sites: A Guide to Preparing for Habitat Improvements on School Grounds, 1993, Western Regional Environmental Education Council

Section III

Plan into Action

"A thing is right when it tends to preserve the integrity, stability and beauty of the biotic community. It is wrong when it tends otherwise."

Aldo Leopold, The Land Ethic

CHAPTER 5 – DEVELOPING THE ENHANCEMENT PLAN

What can you do with your schoolyard property to make it more appealing and useful for wildlife, and to maximize its use by the greatest number of wild species?

CHAPTER 6 – CHOOSING THE ENHANCEMENT PROJECTS

Which projects will provide the most benefits for wildlife on your schoolyard site?

Chapter 5
Developing the Enhancement Plan

The next step in this process is determining your goals and objectives, and developing a plan for carrying them out. Is your site best suited for a colorful and active butterfly garden, but not much more? Or do you have the space and resources to undertake a full-scale enhancement plan, with several different projects?

SETTING OBJECTIVES

The combination of existing conditions and your objectives forms the basis for the enhancement plan. Chapter 6 offers ideas for many habitat enhancement projects you can implement on your schoolyard site. You may want to look through this material to inspire your team with the variety of possibilities, before you develop a plan.

Keep in mind that the projects you select will be directly related to the needs and potential of your unique site.

Applying the Site Inventory

Review the data collected from your site inventory. It should provide the following information:

- what habitat types you have
- which wildlife species are currently using the site
- which wildlife species could potentially use the site, based on available habitat components

It should also provide useful information about how humans are utilizing the site, which will influence your plans for habitat enhancement.

Determining Wildlife Use

To determine what species of wildlife might be found on your site, compile a list of all birds, mammals, reptiles, and amphibians that can be found in your area. Field guides will be a helpful reference. Your list will probably be quite extensive; however, your site will probably not provide for the needs of all of these animals.

The food and cover information you have gathered will provide the foundation for editing your list of species to those that might utilize your site. This is accomplished by comparing the habitat requirements of these species with the habitat your site provides.

Write a descriptive summary of the results from your inventory and wildlife research. This summary will be applied in your enhancement plan. Include both the natural and cultural elements of your site.

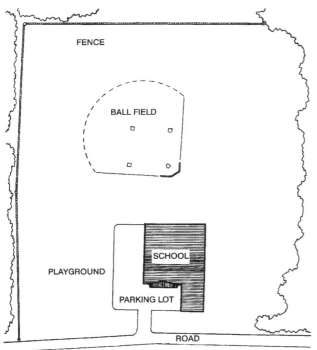

Base Map of Schoolyard

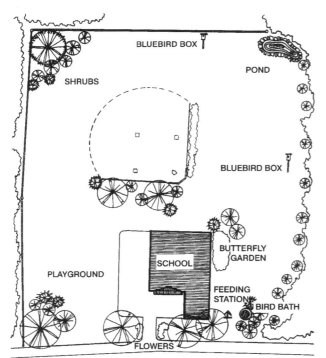

Schoolyard with Enhancements

LEAF-BEARING TREES AND SHRUBS   EVERGREEN TREES AND SHRUBS

DEVELOPING THE ENHANCEMENT PLAN

Once the inventory is complete and your summary written, your team is now prepared to draft an enhancement plan. A written plan will help your wildlife program work most effectively.

The plan is extremely valuable as it provides you with a good foundation from which to launch your efforts, and also a measure of your accomplishments. A good plan is flexible and takes into consideration that the natural world is dynamic.

It can take many years for the natural world to replace what humans can change in a matter of minutes. This fact provides evidence in favor of a well thought-out written plan based on sound ecological principles.

Identifying Your Objectives

The first thing to do when developing a plan is to have your objectives for enhancing your schoolyard site clear in your mind and written down on paper. Decide what you want to achieve, and what you can reasonably accomplish. It may be to invite a few bird species to a courtyard, or you may choose to plant a meadow, build a pond, maintain nest boxes, and encourage a variety of wildlife species. A range of options is available to you.

Invite the diverse ideas of your team members, and incorporate them into the plan. You'll probably find it necessary to negotiate several compromises in this process to effectively meet the needs and expectations of all those involved. Your choices will be determined by your goals and available resources. Consider both short-term (1-5 years) and long-term objectives (5-10 years or more).

A Practical Approach to Objectives

After you clearly state your goal(s), begin to outline the enhancement strategies and methods you will need for implementing your plan.

First, list the various needs and interests relative to human use of the site. What are school policies relative to construction, planting, student use of certain areas?

Next, develop general enhancement objectives based on the results of your inventory and survey. Look these over carefully and ask yourself which objectives are attainable with your available financial and time resources.

Put them in order of priority. You may have to make decisions regarding trade-offs.

As a check on the development of your plan, consider whether the projects you are outlining are:

1. realistic,
2. constructive for wildlife and people, and
3. whether you have the resources to accomplish them.

Compile this information into one plan that can be adjusted as needed to meet your purposes and goals.

Gathering Resources

To make your plans a reality, you will need certain resources, including money, people, and materials. Make a needs list for your plan and identify possible sources of assistance. Should you discover that you lack key resources for implementing your plan in its entirety, you may choose to develop another, smaller plan, or select one component of the current plan that you can successfully implement.

Preparing a Timeline

Whatever the scope of your project, your success will be greatly improved if you prioritize your objectives and prepare a timeline. This may also allow you to gradually carry out, over a longer period of time, a more complex and multi-faceted enhancement plan for which you currently lack certain resources. Plan for both the short term and the long term.

The enhancement of wildlife habitat is a dynamic process that develops and blossoms over time. The outcome of projects you implement may not be exactly what your team had anticipated or planned; other factors may be introduced over time that influence the results. A maintenance plan for your enhancement project(s) (as discussed in Chapter 7) will serve to protect the results from certain human influences, such as vandalism, changing school administrations and/or staff, and human activity around the site.

"Keep it simple."
BILL CARR
MILFORD ELEMENTARY
MILFORD, NH

Evaluation – Measuring Your Plan's Success

Along with your timeline, determine the benefits you anticipate will result from your efforts. Decide what key features, events, or changes you will use to evaluate the project. These could include a change in population level of a species, or the arrival of a desired species that your site has successfully attracted.

Keeping records of the planning and implementation process will help ensure the continuation of the enhancement efforts, even as your working team changes over time. Plan to document the process with sketches, maps, photographs, videos and other tools. This will demonstrate the dynamic development of your site and serve as a measure of your plan's success.

ENHANCEMENT PLAN FORMAT

Overview

If you have carefully and thoroughly applied the information presented so far, you have the foundation on which to write an enhancement plan. Where maps are designed to be quick at-a-glance references, a written plan details the specifics of your habitat resources and approaches to habitat enhancement in one reference.

The plan is a practical tool to help you carry out your team's goals for the school site. It doesn't need to be elaborate or lengthy, but it should be complete. You may find it simpler to prepare it in outline form with lists, diagrams, and sketches to supplement. The finished document should make sense to your working team, but ultimately should be written so that anyone could pick it up and put it into action.

Use the following format as a guide, referring to material in other chapters and the appendices for more in-depth information and specifics. Your needs should dictate the extent to which you develop each of the following components.

Components:

1. School Name and Location: *Where is this taking place?*

2. Purpose Statement: *Why are you doing this project?*
   This is a short statement of your intentions.

3. Working Team: *Who will be involved?*
   List all participating teachers, including grades and subjects taught.
   Indicate if there is a designated leader, or a core group of teachers and/or students who will take charge of the project. (See Chapter 2 for details on team building.)

4. General Site Description: *What does this site look like?*
   Include general information about topography, aspect, slope, and land-scape characteristics of the site, as well as information on abutting land. (See Chapter 4 for site inventory details and activity cards.)

5. Map of the School Site: *What does the site include?*
   This represents the results of your site inventory and mapping re-search, and should include those physical, biological and cultural features that will have a bearing on your project. Include map overlays. (See Chapter 3 for mapping details.)

6. Results of Site Inventory: *What do we have on this site?*
   Describe and list in some detail the features and information collected in your site inventory. Note appropriate information on the map, such as soils, vegetation, human-made structures. Include a list of wildlife species that you might expect to use the site. Comment on availability of the basic elements of wildlife habitat (food, water, cover): what is there, where it is, etc. (Refer to Chapter 4.)

7. Goals and Objectives: *What do we want to enhance on this site?*
   These are short statements of what you hope to accomplish. List and explain the anticipated outcome as benefits to people and to wildlife. List each goal separately, and follow it with the objectives that will help you achieve that goal.

   Goal = general statement that reflects your desires about the site, which may not be measurable.

   Objectives = statements that describe how to accomplish the goals. They are more specific and measurable.

   For example:

   Goal:

   1. To create a small wildlife food and cover patch with year-round wildlife values.

   Objectives:

   1. Acquire food and cover plants using stipend dollars and selection assistance from fish and wildlife agency and Cooperative Extension Service.

   2. Locate suitable location on site.

   3. Plant food and cover plants to best advantage of wildlife. Planting to be accomplished by students from 3rd-6th grades.

   4. Establish permanent funding for maintenance and future enhance-ment efforts.

"To do the plantings, we broke the map up in sections and assigned classes to the plants. In the fifth grade, 120 students with 3 parents got very involved in the planting."
MATT FERGUSON
DEERFIELD COMMUNITY SCHOOL
DEERFIELD, NH

"Try to influence staff and administration to work on scheduling double blocks of classtime. For example, a 5 period week could have 2 doubles and a single on Friday. This could work for all subjects and is a rising need based on a national trend towards project based learning."

DON DAVIS
WESTMORELAND SCHOOL
WESTMORELAND, NH

8. Enhancement Projects: *What will we do to change the site?*
   Indicate what you are enhancing habitat for. You may decide to influence a specific species, you may be working for species diversity, or you may attempt to combine the two (manage for diversity while placing an emphasis on one or two favored species.) List the enhancement projects you intend to implement, and be specific about how and where you will implement them. Provide a complete list of potential options.

9. Timeline: *When will all this happen?*
   Supply specifics on how you will accomplish the objectives. Do more than reiterate your objectives here. For instance, what types of lesson plans will be created to incorporate the wildlife food and cover patch into the curriculum? Are there any state curriculum guidelines you must follow?

   Include:
   – a 1-year plan in some detail, with a prioritized list of all projects, a budget, work teams, and target dates
   – a 5-year plan with a general overview of objectives, anticipated projects and completion dates

   These two plans should be related. Be sure to plan for possible changes that may arise from, for example, changes in project supervision (i.e. teacher turnover), vandalism, failure or success of certain enhancement projects, changes in the use of the school property or new building construction, etc.

10. Resources: *Where can we get assistance?*
    List real potential sources of materials, funding, labor, etc., that will be needed to carry out your plan. How much will your plan cost? Potential donors will want to know. This should not only include where the money might come from, but also some idea of costs for specific elements of the plan.

11. Maintenance Plan: *How can we be sure it will last?*
    This should include information on what needs to be done, in addition to who will do it. Include the costs of maintenance in your budget.

12. Evaluation Method: *How well did we do it?*
    This section should contain specific methods or procedures you will use to assess how well the goals and objectives are being met. Determine ways to measure and evaluate your plan's success. It may be the documented arrival of a certain species, an increase in the population of a species, or occupation of nest boxes that you've installed. Consider establishing an evaluation committee that reviews the plan and the budget annually to assess accomplishments and progress.

Remember to maintain written and photographic records to assist in your evaluation.

Material for this chapter excerpted or adapted with permission from:

Wildlife Habitat Improvement Series, David Langley, University of New Hampshire Cooperative Extension, 1993

✍ **Activities from the Project WILD activity guide** relating to wildlife management and plans.

Grades	Title	Topic
2-3	Can Do!	school environment projects
3-4	Can Do!	school environment projects
4-6	Can Do!	school environment projects
	Improving Wildlife Habitat in the Community	habitat improvement projects
	Planning for People and Wildlife	community planning
7-9	Can Do!	school environment projects
	Improving Wildlife Habitat in the Community	habitat improvement projects
	Planning for People and Wildlife	community planning
	Rainfall and the Forest	rainfall, vegetation, habitat

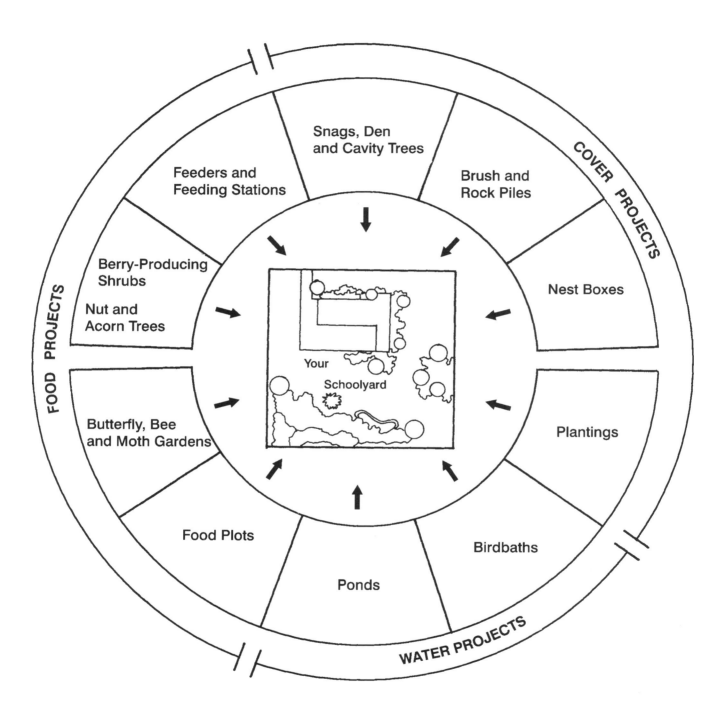

Chapter 6
Choosing the Enhancement Projects

Several criteria can be used to select a wildlife enhancement project. Depending on your goals, you may want a project your whole team can be involved in, or one that is most compatible with some other activity underway on your site.

CHOOSING A PROJECT

To help you in choosing a project, we have prepared two charts. The first has six sets of criteria: location, action, wildlife habitat needs supplied, cost, time commitment, and longevity or durability. Each of the project groups in this chapter is rated for each set of criteria.

The second chart can be used as a guide to determine some of the wildlife species you can expect to attract or enhance by each project. This is only a guide; it cannot be precise since many factors besides the project itself determine what wildlife occur in your area. Nevertheless, if you are particularly interested in one species of bird or mammal, Table 2 will help you identify some of the projects that are most likely to enhance that species.

At the end of each project group is a list of related literature, which is fully referenced in Appendix H. We recommend you explore these before starting work. Appendix J includes a checklist for action projects.

Attracting Native Wildlife

As you are considering your enhancement project(s), learn as much as you can about the wildlife species you wish to influence. This will not only add to your enjoyment, appreciation and understanding of these creatures, but will also help you be more successful with your project(s).

Above all, be realistic in your expectations. Work with species that are common to your area and do not expect overnight results. Time is an important factor in attempting to influence population levels of any wildlife species.

Remember, it is better to undertake a small project and execute it well than to attempt too much and not be able to see it through, for a number of possible reasons, to a successful conclusion.

Project Codes

While the projects are listed and discussed by the primary habitat features they enhance, you'll notice on the chart that each project often serves more than one purpose. Refer back to Chapter 2 "Concepts" for a discussion of each of the principle components of habitat.

Food
1. Feeding stations
2. Plantings and plants

Water
3. Water projects

Cover
4. Brush shelters and rockpiles
5. Den and cavity trees and snags
6. Nest structures

	Project Type					
	Food		Water		Cover	
Criteria	1	2	3	4	5	6
Location						
Around the Building	x	x	x		x	
Schoolyard	x	x	x		x	x
Woodlot	x	x	x	x	x	x
Fields and other open areas	x	x	x	x		x
Action						
Plant		x				
Dig		x	x			
Cut	x	x	x	x		x
Build	x		x	x		x
Maintain		x			x	
Wildlife Habitat Needs Supplied						
Food	x	x		x		
Cover		x		x	x	x
Water			x			
Cost						
Low		x	x	x	x	
Medium	x	x	x			x
High				x	x	
Time Commitment						
Low		x	x	x	x	
Medium	x	x	x			
High		x				

	Food		Water		Cover	
	1	2	3	4	5	6
Longevity or Durability						
Low		x				
Medium		x	x	x	x	
High	x	x			x	x
Wildlife Species Enhanced						
Mammals						
White-tailed deer		x	x	x		
Cottontail rabbit		x		x		
Gray squirrel	x	x	x		x	x
Raccoon		x	x		x	x
Skunk		x		x		
Mink			x	x		
Weasel				x		
Chipmunk	x	x		x	x	
White-footed mouse		x		x		
Bat						x
Birds						
Wild Turkey	x	x	x	x		
Ruffed grouse		x	x	x		
Owls					x	x
Hawks					x	
Wood duck		x			x	x
Chickadee	x	x			x	
Cardinal	x	x				
Bluebird		x			x	x
Mourning Dove	x	x	x			
Wren						x
Bob-white quail				x	x	
Hummingbird	x	x				
Insects						
Butterflies and Moths		x				
Bees		x		x		
Reptiles						
Turtles		x	x			
Snakes		x	x			
Amphibians						
Frogs		x	x			
Salamanders		x	x			
Toads		x	x			

(Charts adapted with permission from Decker, D.J. and J.W. Kelley. 1981. Enhancement of Wildlife Habitat on Private Lands. cornel Info. Bull. 181. NYS College of Agriculture and Life Sciences, Cornell University, Ithaca.)

FOOD IMPROVEMENTS

Feeders and Feeding Stations

Key points to consider:
- **Feeders are primarily a wintertime project.**
- **You will need to:**
    - **provide a variety of foods and placement areas.**
    - **keep feeders filled.**
    - **protect feeders from unwanted visitors.**
    - **provide cover for protection from predators.**

Although planting or maintaining naturally occurring food plants is probably the best way to supply wildlife food, you may choose to feed animals "artificially." This approach provides food when other sources may not be readily available, and enhances your observation of wildlife while they are feeding.

FEEDER GUIDELINES

1. For best results, feeders should be set up in the fall before cold weather. Feeding stations are most effective and most used in winter months.
2. Once established, keep food available at all times and do not let the food supply run out until spring. Birds will depend on it after they have been using it for only a short time.
3. Any platform type feeder where you are offering seeds and grains should be roofed and protected from rain and snow so the food will stay dry and not spoil.
4. A feeding station should be made cat-proof if it is on a post, pole or tree.
5. With the station placed fairly close to the building, you can enjoy watching the birds and also keep a check on the food supply. However, take care with windows and other reflective surfaces so the birds don't fly into them. Cut silhouettes of raptors from dark paper, and tape them to the windows to deter birds from flying too close.
6. Feeders will be more effective if located near some kind of escape cover, such as bushes or shrubs.
7. Remember to clean feeders periodically.

(Excerpted with permission from Environmental Awareness: Wildlife, *Otis F. Curtis, University of Connecticut Cooperative Extension System.)*

Artificial feeding is typically a winter activity, this being the time of food scarcity for wildlife in snowy climates. Birds most frequently are the object of winter feeding, but some people choose to feed other animals, such as squirrels. (The practice is not recommended for some species, such as deer, for reasons of expense, nutrition, and artificially concentrating a population in one area. In addition, it may be illegal.)

When you decide to provide food for wildlife over winter, realize you have assumed a major responsibility for the duration of the winter. You are creating an artificial situation because often you are concentrating a relatively large number of animals in an area that cannot support them naturally. Should you not provide enough food or stop feeding before natural food is abundant again in spring, many of the animals could die.

Remember to locate feeding stations in places with protective cover nearby to shelter the feeding animals from wind and predators, especially house cats.

Feeding Birds

Birds have a high metabolic rate (the speed with which they produce energy), and must eat large amounts of high-energy food often, and rapidly. This is true year-round, but is especially critical in winter when nights last about 15 hours in the northern United States.

There is some disagreement among wildlife professionals on the need to maintain an uninterrupted feeding program during the winter months. It is likely that most birds have more than one site to visit for food and foraging, and if your feeder is empty now and then, they will move on to the next location. Ideally, it should be replenished morning and evening. Studies show that wintering birds begin to feed at dawn and stop about mid-afternoon.

Like humans, birds have definite preferences for what they like to eat and how they like to eat it. There are seed-eaters, fruit-lovers, and birds that consume the concentrated calories in animal fat. Likewise, there are birds
that eat at ground level and birds that prefer to feed at different heights off the ground.

Obviously, the more you know about their food preferences, and the more you cater to those preferences by offering a variety of food at
your feeders, the greater variety of birds you can attract to your schoolyard. Selective feeding lures specific kinds of birds.

Various types of feeding stations can be constructed. These can be simple or elaborate affairs. Some are merely board platforms where foods are placed; others are deluxe models. In any case, there are certain guidelines which should be followed with any feeding station.

For details on types of feeders, food, and placement refer to:

> *Planting an Oasis for Wildlife,*
> National Wildlife Federation
> Urban Institute Wildlife Manager's
> Notebook #3, "Feeding Birds in
> Winter."
> *The Bird Feeder Book,* Donald and
> Lillian Stokes.
> *Environmental Awareness: Wildlife,*
> Otis Curtis.

BIRDS SEEM TO PREFER FEEDING AT ONE OF FOUR LEVELS:

1. Mourning doves, sparrows, towhees, and juncos are ground feeders.
2. Cardinals, finches, jays, and sparrows feed on raised or table-level feeders.
3. Titmice, and goldfinches prefer to feed from hanging feeders.
4. Suet eaters (like woodpeckers, nutchatches, and wrens) prefer to use tree trunks while feeding.

Some birds feed at more than one level. These are not hard and fast rules, and in a particularly severe winter, birds will seek food wherever it is available. Normally, however, birds will fill an eating "niche," and it is ideal to have food at the various levels to attract all kinds of birds.

(Urban Wildlife Manager's Notebook–3, "Feeding Birds in Winder." Urban Wildlife Resources, 5130 West Running Brook Rd., Columbia, MD 21044)

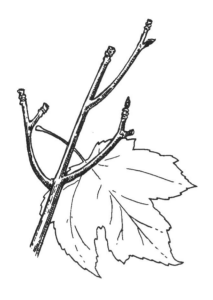

Plantings and Plants

Key points to consider:

- **Consider the characteristics of your site, including soils and climate.**
- **Use native species.**
- **Provide plants that will prosper in different seasons.**
- **Allow space for the growth of your plantings.**
- **Plan for continuing care and maintenance for certain plantings.**

Plants are valuable in many ways to the wildlife using your schoolyard. They provide food, shelter and nest sites. Strategic plantings of cover-producing conifers, food-bearing shrubs, and plots of grain, cover and grass can turn your site into a paradise for a variety of birds and mammals.

Plantings need not be extensive, but should meet the year-round habitat requirements of wildlife. For example, plots of clover and grass may be fine for summer and early fall food, but do not provide much food during the winter months. The key is to provide a wide diversity of habitat conditions.

Working with plants to improve your site for wildlife can be a very rewarding experience if you approach the activity with common sense, some basic knowledge of the plants, and a reasonable plan of action. There are many sources of good information on this subject. See the Instructional Resources List in Appendix H.

THE CASE FOR NATIVE PLANTS

When deciding on which plants to use, select those native to your ara. While some exotic plants are excellent and are recommended for certain application, native species have passed the text of time for ecological suitability and ave few of the limitations or risks that may be experienced with exotic species. They ared better adapted to the area, require less maintenance, and resist the extremes of cold, heat, drought, and wetness.

Use and improve upon what you alreadyhaveon your property first. Then it might be appropriate tot ry a new species or add a species not locally abundant but native to the area.

Never remove plants from the wild because they generally do not survivewhen transplanted. In addition, removal of wildlife plants could harm natural communities, and it may be illegal. Contact your local garden club or extension office for information.

Appendix E lists a variety of trees, shrubs, etc, that have been selected for their proven enhancement value to wildlife habitat. From this list of plants, single species or combinations of species could be planted to establish new vegetation to meet a variety of objectives, depending on the characteristics of the planting site or the species of wildlife of interest.

Don't expect too much from your plantings for the first few years. It will take some time for the plants to become established and provide adequate food and cover for wildlife.

While considering your budget and what is available, keep in mind that the seedlings you plant will grow and fill out. Try to envision what you want the area to look like in 5 to 10 years, and plan accordingly. If you are limited by funds or space, shrubs and dense cover plants would be more desirable than trees, since they provide habitat more quickly and at a comparatively lower cost than larger shade trees.

For quick growth, beautiful color, wildlife food and cover, erosion control and general outdoor studies, it's hard to beat berry-producing shrubs. Many shrubs, when planted as seedlings, will obtain a height of six to eight feet in four to five years. Due to their smaller size at maturity, shrubs can be spaced closer together than trees.

When planning your habitat improvement area, consider site factors such as soil fertility, soil moisture, slope of the land, the present amount of sunlight and the amount that will be available in the future when trees and shrubs reach maturity.

> ### BENEFITS OF NATIVE PLANTS
>
> - Native plants are naturally adapted to the soil, rainfall, and sunlight conditions of your region. They are apt to thrive once established, and to require less maintenance.
>
> - Native plants form the food base that wildlife species depend on. Their presence will attract wildlife species that don't normally come into residential areas.
>
> - Non-native plant species often lack the natural controls that help keep their populations in check. As they proliferate, they choke out the native plant species.
>
> *(Excerpted with permission from Creating Landscapes for Wildlife: A Guide for Backyards in Utah, Nordstrom, Sue and Margy Halpin, Department of Landscape Architecture and Environmental Planning, Utah State University and Utah Division of Wildlife Resources, 1991.)*

Plants for wildlife can be obtained from a number of sources. Modest changes on a limited budget can be achieved by purchasing plants through your regional forester or commercial nurseries, by obtaining permission from a rural landowner to remove wildlife tree or shrub seedlings from his or her land for transplanting, or growing your own from seeds. See Appendix I for more information.

Native Plant Communities Restoration

Some school sites may have an area large enough to undertake a native plant restoration project; for example, filling or draining a beaver pond, or restoring a woodland or forest, wetland, or prairie. If you have a large section of the school site that you wish to restore to native vegetation, contact your local forester, arboretum, the botany department of a nearby college or university, or local department of natural resources to learn what original plant species are characteristic of your area.

Mast-producing Trees

Mast, the nuts and acorns from a variety of trees, is an important source of food for many species of wildlife. Deer, turkey, squirrel, and raccoon are probably the best known mast users.

Should you have a few mast trees on your schoolyard site, such as hickory, beech, oak, or walnut, you can improve nut or acorn production and the

overall health of the trees through several management practices. As a beginning, it might be best to select only one or two trees to work on to gain experience and to evaluate the results of your efforts. Contact your local forester for information and assistance. See Appendix G for details.

Food Plot Planting

In areas where cover is abundant, food plot planting can provide a valuable source of grain and green vegetation. Food plots should always be planted near permanent cover, as they usually provide little protection of their own during winter. Small plots provide enough food for most wildlife species. Many wildlife species use them at various times of the year.

Herbaceous cover plantings, such as sweet clover, red clover, alfalfa, and grasses, are excellent for attracting small wildlife. They can be planted in strips, 15 to 20 feet wide, in a fallow area of the grounds. Strips can be spaced to alternate plant types, and to allow strips of natural vegetation to grow in between.

Planting strips of grains such as corn, rye, etc., can provide a good food and cover source. A typical food plot would be about 10 feet wide and perhaps 100 feet in length. Allow the grain to stand over the winter to provide good cover for rabbits, birds, and other small animals. Plant a variety of different grains to observe and study.

Planting and food plots require good seedbed preparation and fertilization. Planting dates, seed sources and information may be obtained from your local Soil Conservation Service district office or Extension Service. See Appendix F for details. Seed can also be purchased at a farm supply store or ordered at a garden store. See Appendix I for more information.

(Excerpted from Guidelines and Features for Outdoor Classrooms, Indiana Department of Natural Resources, Division of Forestry.)

Butterfly and Container Gardens

Even with limited space for a garden in your schoolyard, or an entirely paved site, you can attract butterflies, moths, hummingbirds, and orioles to a container garden. Wooden barrels, boxes built from railroad ties, and window boxes are three possible containers for wildflower plantings.

Native wildflowers provide food for caterpillars and nectar for adult butterflies and certain birds. The seeds these flowers produce also are an excellent source of winter food for numerous bird species.

Wildflowers particularly attractive to wildlife include the milkweeds, asters or phlox, black- and brown-eyed susans, white or purple bergamot, cardinal flower, and goldenrods. Numerous domestic or cultivated flowers are also attractive to butterflies, moths, bees and hummingbirds.

Many of the best bee and butterfly plants are herbs.

For more information, *Landscaping for Wildlife*, by Carrol Henderson, contains many plans and lists for butterfly and container gardens. Also consult the Urban Wildlife Manager's Notebook #11 "Urban Insects II: Butterflies in Your Garden." These and other helpful references are listed in Appendix H.

WATER IMPROVEMENTS

Key points to consider:

- **Sources of water can be simple or sophisticated projects.**
- **Utilize on-site sources of water.**
- **Check your school's liability insurance for precautions.**

Not all wildlife need standing or free-running water to sustain themselves, but some do, and many that do not require these conditions still seem to prefer them. In fact, no matter how abundant food is on your site, many species of wildlife will not use the site unless water is available for drinking and bathing.

Simple Water Projects

A simple birdbath will meet minimum requirements. However, a garden pond is inviting to both wildlife and people, and need not be expensive nor complicated. Keep in mind that a pond for learning can be as small as a shallow reflecting pool, teeming with live microscopic specimens.

Because of increased liability pressures placed on schools, it is sometimes not feasible to build a pond. You may also be required to hold a permit. Many of the same benefits of having a large pond can be obtained by constructing a small, shallow, watering hole for wildlife. This structure can be as small as a child's wading pool and still abound with life from aquatic plants and micro-organisms to tadpoles and minnows. If located near the school building where electricity is available, a small pump can be used to create a waterfall and circulate the water.

Simple options include: 1. a hole dug and filled with water (for areas with non-porous, clay soil) 2. a hole lined with a flexible liner, 3. a pre-formed pool sunk in a hole, or 4. a "tub pool" sunk to ground level. If a deeper pond is desired, check the school's liability insurance to see what additional precautions are needed.

Ponds

A pond on the school site can provide excellent opportunities for students to observe and study aquatic plants and animals. Ponds also provide students with firsthand experiences in managing water resource problems and solutions.

If the pond is 1/2 acre or larger and has a minimum depth of 8 feet over 25 percent of the area, or a minimum of 6 feet over 50 percent of the area, it can probably support a healthy fish population of bluegill and largemouth bass. A soil conservationist or fish biologist can advise how to properly stock and manage your pond.

Many aquatic plants seed themselves naturally. You may also transplant a variety of aquatic plants around the shoreline for diversity. A variety of trees, shrubs, legumes, and grasses around the pond area will attract more wildlife.

If your school does not have a pond but is interested in constructing one, consult with your local soil conservationist. S/he can investigate the feasibility of a pond on your site.

Marshes and Wetlands—
Identifying and Using Sources of Fresh Water

Does your school have any wet areas on the grounds? Most school sites do have a few. Poorly drained areas can be very difficult for maintenance crews to mow and nearly useless as a playground or athletic field. These "troublesome" wet spots are often capable of being developed into nature's most productive wildlife and outdoor learning area, a marsh.

To be properly developed, a marsh should have 25% of its area excavated to a depth of about three feet and the remaining 75% to less than three feet deep. This will encourage the growth of cattails, bulrushes, sedges, reeds, and other aquatic plants. In addition, plant wildlife food plants and shrubs around your marsh.

Permits may be required to alter any wetlands areas. Check with your local wetlands board or state department of natural resources..

(Excerpted from *Guidelines and Features for Outdoor Classrooms*, Indiana Department of Natural Resources, Division of Forestry.)

Enhancing Wildlife Habitat on Private Lands, by Dawson and Kelly, includes several good ideas for water projects to do with ordinary tools, and a reference list.

"The children planted the trees lovingly."

EILEEN BELYEA
PIERMONT SCHOOL
PIERMONT, NH

COVER IMPROVEMENTS

Den and Cavity Tree Preservation

Key points to consider:

- **Snag and den trees can be created using available trees on the site.**
- **Contact your county forester or regional wildlife biologist for assistance.**

For some kinds of wildlife, dead trees are more useful than living ones. Countless insects burrow into decaying wood during their life cycles. Woodpeckers, nuthatches, and wrens search tree surfaces to find this insect food. Woodpeckers also excavate nesting and roosting cavities in the soft tissues of decaying trees. In turn, these cavities are sought by "secondary cavity nesters"-birds and mammals that cannot create their own cavities.

Probably the most critical components of cover are nest sites. Nest sites can take many forms, but those most frequently in scarce supply are tree cavities. The scarcity of nesting and roosting cavities is a major factor limiting the populations and diversity of many cavity-nesting birds.

Snags, Den Trees, and Wolf Trees

Snags — dead trees that are still standing — are used primarily as nesting, feeding or perching sites for birds and small mammals like squirrels and raccoons.

Den trees are those trees having the trunk or large limbs hollowed out by rotting, with an opening to the outside. This includes some snags, of course, but den trees typically are still alive and often continue to bear mast or fruit. Den trees are used by mammals varying in size from a mouse to a black bear. Many birds use den trees, and so do honey bees.

Wolf trees — large, spreading trees that were left to provide shade, or for nut or syrup production, when pastures were cleared and, hence, became the "lone wolf" — are likely to be den trees. These trees also tend to produce more mast or fruit than others, making them doubly valuable to wildlife.

Most areas do not have enough snags and den trees. These can be created using available trees on the land. If you have few or no snags or den trees currently, you may want to build and place nest boxes for birds and mammals. These can serve as substitutes for natural cavities.

Talk to your local forester about identifying and maintaining snags that may be on your schoolyard property. Also, consult the Urban Wildlife Manager's Notebook #12, "Saving Snags for Urban Wildlife."

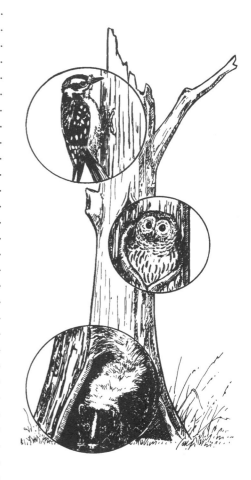

Nesting Structures

Key points to consider:

– **Nest structures can be provided for many species of birds
  and small mammals.**
– **Placement and care are critical for health and optimum use.**
– **Build species-appropriate structures using design specifications
  (see Appendix F).**

Creation of natural cavities can be enhanced by timber practices, like cutting, but these usually take a long time before they become suitable places for cavity nesting wildlife. You may want to provide nest structures for some types of wildlife that would find food, water, and other cover requirements on your site right now. These artificial homes can take many forms, including bat boxes, squirrel boxes, various songbird boxes, and wood duck nest boxes.

Wildlife that use nest boxes find their natural homes in the holes and hollows of dead and decaying trees. They choose their nest and den sites in the types of habitats that can support their young. The type of nest boxes to build depends on the species you are interested in attracting and the type of habitat that is found on your property.

Bird Nest Boxes

The actual needs of cavity-nesting birds are few and often may be met by a small expenditure of time and work. To make the nesting facilities safer and more suitable for the occupants, certain principles of construction, design, and location should be observed.

Materials: For constructing birdhouses, wood is the best building material. Avoid using metal. It gets too hot when exposed to the sun. Sawmill waste — rough slabs with the bark on — furnishes cheap and satisfactory material for rustic nest boxes. Use wood of 1/2 to 7/8 inch thickness. Thoroughly seasoned pine, cypress or cedar, free from knots, is most desirable. Use galvanized nails, brass screws, and hinges for permanency, since these are exposed to the weather.

Dimensions and elevation: Build the house for some particular species native to your region, not just a 'bird house.' For best results, follow specifications as to size of house, diameter and location of entrance hole, and location of the box.

Paint: Where a rustic finish is not sought, paint greatly improves the weathering qualities of birdhouses. Dull tones of brown, gray, or green are generally the best choices. Martin houses and others placed in exposed situations should be painted white to reflect heat.

Protection from rain: Roofs should be made with sufficient pitch to shed water readily, with the overhang extending 2-3 inches to protect the entrance hole. The opening of the nest cavity itself can be bored at an upward slant to aid in keeping out water. Provide drainage holes in the bottom of the box to reduce danger of drowning young birds in heavy storms.

Protection from predators: Place the box where the birds may be free from danger of cats, or place a galvanized tin cat-guard on the approach to the box (pole or tree). All nest boxes should be protected by a predator guard.

Protection from heat: If attention is paid to the principles of cool construction, the suffering of nestlings during periods of excessive heat can be lessened. Wood is, in itself, a fairly good heat insulator, but the interior of the average nest box is small; a single opening near the top permits little ventilation. Ventilate the box by small auger holes or a slit just under the roof, to give limited air circulation without producing drafts.

Accessibility: Put up only a few bird boxes in a limited area, spaced according to the territorial needs of each species. All birdhouses should be placed so they are readily accessible, and built so they are easily opened, inspected and cleaned. Birds should not be disturbed when nesting. After each brood of birds, remove the old nest and thoroughly clean the box to prevent the multiplication of parasites.

Entrances: Since entrance holes for birdhouses are usually near the top, the lumber used, if dressed (i.e., trimmed, planed boards), should be roughened, grooved, or cleated to assist the young in climbing to the opening. Perches on the outside, below the opening, are unnecessary (since only house sparrows and starlings use a perch), and seem more of an assistance to predators.

Placement: Wooded fence rows, grassy meadows, forested areas and the banks of ponds and creeks are good locations for nesting boxes. Hollow trees, old fence posts and burrows in the ground can be existing natural nesting sites.

Appendix F gives the proper nest box dimensions for various species and the height at which boxes should be placed above the ground. When considering nesting boxes, keep other animals besides birds in mind. Nesting structures for squirrels, bats, and ground nesting mammals are also easily constructed. Artificial dens may alleviate a housing shortage and attract these animals to areas where food is available. A wildlife biologist can provide specifications and information on what kinds of nesting boxes to build for your area. Contact your state fish and wildlife agency.

"Bat boxes can be built by 8th grade students in a non-shop classroom if you remember to: 1) pre-cut all lumber; 2) label specific pieces with marker as A, B, C, etc.; 3) team carpenters by twos; 4) consider screws versus nails."

CHUCK MINER
HOOKSETT MEMORIAL SCHOOL
HOOKSETT, NH

In addition, we recommend the following resources:

- *Woodworking for Wildlife*, by Carrol Henderson
- *Enhancing Wildlife Habitat on Private Lands,* Cornell University
- *Planting an Oasis for Wildlife* in National Wildlife Federation's "Gardening with Wildlife Kit"
- Urban Wildlife Manager's Notebook #4

See Appendix H for details.

Wildlife Brush Shelters

Brush shelters serve primarily as cover for wildlife. Many species of small mammals use this type of cover when available, but brush piles are especially important to cottontail rabbits.

In winter, a brushpile may provide cover for sparrows, rabbits and shrews and, if the base underneath contains substantial limbs or logs, cover for hibernating salamanders and wood-boring insects. In summer, the same brushpile will be a cool retreat and a nesting site for a similar variety of animals.

If the brushpile can be located near or adjacent to cover, 'travel lanes' from place to place will benefit the more secretive animals like reptiles, amphibians, and mammals. Fence corners, woodland borders, meadow edges, or similar sites, if available, are ideal locations for brushpiles.

Refer to Urban Wildlife Manager's Notebook– 9, "Rockpiles and Brushpiles" for detailed instructions on brushpile construction.

Living brush piles provide food in addition to shelter for a variety of small mammals. Those of the hardwood species may supply buds, twigs, and foliage for several years. Because insects use the brush piles for cover and to eat the foliage, the piles also benefit many species of songbirds that forage for the insects. You can make two basic kinds of living brush piles, using either a conifer or several deciduous trees. Their location depends upon the location of the trees to be used. *Enhancement of Wildlife Habitat on Private Lands*, by Dawson and Kelly, includes instructions.

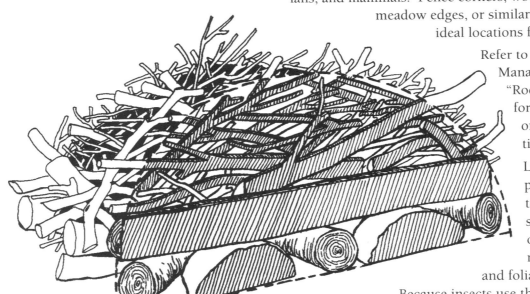

Cross-section of a brush pile

Rockpiles as Shelter

Amphibians and reptiles are attracted to rockpiles to avoid predators and to regulate their body temperatures. Woodland salamanders seek moisture next to the ground under rocks, and toads rest in the shaded nooks and crannies, waiting for dark when they emerge to hunt insects. Reptiles bask on the rocks to absorb radiated heat, but move out of the sun when the heat is too intense. These herptiles (reptiles and amphibians) may hibernate within or under suitable rockpiles in colder climates.

Worms, slugs, and insects can be found in the sheltered, damp areas under rocks, and are a source of food for herptiles, birds and small mammals. Rockpiles placed near underbrush or openings in wooded areas tend to attract chipmunks, if there are also nut, seed, and berry producing plants in the area.

Urban Wildlife Manager's Notebook - 9, "Rockpiles and Brushpiles" provides detailed information and instructions.

OTHER PROJECTS

Creating Openings and Edges

If your schoolyard site is forest-covered, and by itself or together with adjacent property forms a large woodland tract (10 acres or larger), consider creating an area of open space. A forest clearing can enhance the overall animal diversity of an area because it normally produces herbs, grasses, brush, and younger forest stages of plant growth.

This diversity of plant types and sizes provides more kinds of food and nest sites than does a solid stand of forest. The brush accumulated from the cutting operation can be made into brush piles, placed in and along the perimeter of the opening.

Contact your county forester for assistance. See Appendix G for a listing.

Releasing Wild Apple Trees

Wild apple trees are among the most valuable wildlife food resources that we have. They are commonly found on rural lands where they provide food for a wide variety of wildlife. The apples, leaves, buds, twigs and even the bark may be used by various birds and mammals over the course of a year.

Although much of the rural northeast has apple trees growing in the wild or unattended on abandoned homesteads, many of these important wildlife plants are being lost each year to overcrowding by forest species that eventually invade and dominate the site. The life span, health, and productivity of these apple trees can be improved by applying some simple techniques in common use by foresters and orchardists.

If you have wild apple trees in a wooded area or overgrown field on your property, contact your county forester for information and assistance.

Meadows as Alternatives to Lawns

Establishing a meadow area is a logical first step to creating a natural landscape around one's school. Plant diversity encourages wildlife diversity.

By reducing the lawn area to that necessary only for student recreation, or to satisfy the school's desire for a plot of clipped grass for aesthetics, a more diverse and interesting landscape can be created. Native wildflowers and grasses can be grown in unmowed areas. These will attract seed-eating birds like finches, small native mammals, and pollinating invertebrates like butterflies.

See "Urban Wildlife Manager's Notebook – 5, "Natural Landscaping — Meadows" for more information.

Student Efforts in Enhancement Activities

Students can:

- plant trees, shrubs and flowers
- construct nest boxes and feeding stations
- build brushpiles and rockpiles
- make signs
- fill feeders
- water plantings
- clear trails of small fallen branches and young growth

The age and abilities of the children will determine to what extent they get involved. Younger children require more supervision and can handle lighter tasks. Older children can work more independently with more complex or physically-demanding tasks.

The children may work by classroom groups or in small groups, or you can schedule an all-school work day and have everyone participate in enhancement efforts. Work groups can be arranged, mixing children of all age levels, with parents and other volunteers providing supervision and support. All this will be determined by the people power you have available and how much scheduling and planning your team is willing to do. For details on team building, refer to Chapter 1 and to *WILD School Sites: A Guide to Preparing for Wildlife Habitat Improvement Projects on School Grounds.*

"Troubleshooting" — How to Get the Wildlife You Want

The key for dealing with an uninvited visitor is to understand reasons for the animal's behavior and then remove the feature that is attracting the animal.

"The HOME project was rejuvenating for us. We worked on our nature trail, updated maps, and had the local conservation society donate bluebird boxes. We're planning a guided walking tour with a brochure and map."

PAT CUSHING
NORTH HAMPTON SCHOOL
NORTH HAMPTON, NH

To minimize problems with wildlife in urban and suburban areas:

1. For buildings, screen exposed beams, ledges, and unscreened eave ventilation holes, or other nooks, holes, and crannies likely to be occupied by house sparrows, starlings, and pigeons.

2. Be sure lids of garbage containers are tightly secured to prevent entry by raccoons, dogs, rats, or other unwelcome visitors.

3. Install substantial screening or other devices on chimneys to prevent access by raccoons, squirrels, bats and birds.

4. In some situations, changes in plant types and date or depth of planting are helpful in reducing damage to vegetation. Your county agricultural agent may be able to give advice on this.

5. Squirrel interference with bird feeding can be reduced or eliminated by using counter-balanced or other available types of squirrel-proof feeders.

6. Insects like mosquitoes and grasshoppers can be considered a nuisance. By providing the right habitat components, you can encourage insect-eating predators like bats, purple martins, dragonflies, tree swallows and bluebirds. This is ecologically more compatible with the environment than solving insect problems with "bug zappers" or harmful chemicals.

More ideas can be found in *A Guide to Urban Wildlife Management* (see Instructional Resources list, Appendix H).

(Adapted with permission from Leedy, D. L., and L. W. Adams. 1984. <u>A Guide to Urban Wildlife Management.</u> Natl. Inst. for Urban Wildlife., Columbia, MD. 42 pp.)

Materials for this chapter excerpted or adapted with permission from:

Barnes, T.G. (ed). 1992. *Private Lands Wildlife Management: A Technical Guidance Manual and Correspondence Course.* University of Kentucky Agricultural Extension Publication, Lexington, KY

Curtis, Otis F., *Environmental Awareness: Wildlife*, University of Connecticut Cooperative Extension System

Decker, D. J., and J. W. Kelley. *Enhancing Wildlife Habitat on Private Lands*, Cornell Inf. Bull. 181. NYS College of Agriculture and Life Sciences, Cornell University, Ithaca, NY, 1981

Henderson, Carrol L. *Landscaping for Wildlife.* Minnesota Department of Natural Resources, St. Paul, 1987

Guidelines and Features for Outdoor Classrooms, Indiana Department of Natural Resources, Division of Forestry

Leedy, D. L., and L. W. Adams. *A Guide to Urban Wildlife Management.* National Institute for Urban Wildlife, Columbia, MD, 1984

Mason, C. Russell, and William A. Taylor. *Help the Birds Find a Home.* Massachusetts Audubon Society, Lincoln, MA

National Institute for Urban Wildlife, Urban Wildlife Manager's Notebooks - #2, *A Simple Backyard Pond*, #3, *Feeding Birds in Winter*, #5, *Natural Landscaping — Meadows*, #9, *Rockpiles and Brushpiles*, #12, *Saving Snags for Wildlife.* Columbia, MD

National Wildlife Federation, *Planting an Oasis for Wildlife.* Washington, D.C., 1986

Nordstrom, Sue and Margy Halpin, *Creating Landscapes for Wildlife: A Guide for Backyards in Utah.* Department of Landscape Architecture and Environmental Planning, Utah State University, and Utah Division of Wildlife Resources, 1991

Section IV
Future Planning

"A land ethic, then, reflects the existence of an ecological conscience, and this in turn reflects a conviction of individual responsibility for the health of the land."

Aldo Leopold, The Land Ethic

CHAPTER 7 – MAINTAINING AND SUSTAINING THE OUTDOOR CLASSROOM

How do we keep the project alive?

EPILOGUE – HABITAT FOR THE FUTURE

Where do we go from here?

Chapter 7
Maintaining and Sustaining the Outdoor Classroom

The greatest challenge, once a project has been established, is to sustain it. That is also one of the most important concerns.

BENEFITS OF MAINTENANCE

Ongoing maintenance of projects has three primary benefits. It will ensure the continuation of your enhancement efforts, and the success of your project. Since it will keep focus on the project and involve a -network of people, it will help deter vandalism. Finally, maintenance will remain as an excellent vehicle for teaching future classes about wildlife needs and human responsibilities.

This is a good time to reflect on earlier discussions in this guide concerning team building, undesirable wildlife, and vandalism. As indicated in Chapter 5, the maintenance plan is developed as part of your enhancement plan, and takes into consideration such factors as the team members, funding, and evaluation of success.

THE NEED FOR A MAINTENANCE PROGRAM

A good maintenance program is essential to both the initial and long term success of your enhancement efforts. At least two people from the team should have primary responsibility for designing a maintenance plan for the project. *Be sure to involve the head of your school's custodial staff in your maintenance plan.* List what the short and long-term maintenance requirements are and who will be responsible for each. The complexity of your maintenance plan will depend on which projects you have chosen to implement and over what period of time. Unnecessary maintenance can be kept to a minimum by keeping plans simple. If the project can't be easily maintained by your team, you may want to reconsider developing it.

A DIFFERENT APPROACH TO MAINTENANCE

Natural landscapes are dynamic; they are always changing. This active quality contributes to the diversity of a landscape and its value to wildlife. By contrast, our manicured schoolyards are static, and most of our maintenance techniques are aimed at keeping things the same. Moreover, the raking, pruning, mowing, and clipping removes nutrients and energy from the landscape.

A fruitful approach is to let your site be dynamic. Let it change, and open the doors to diversity. This approach can be exuberant or modest.

Simply, when leaves or glass clippings are raked from some areas, rather than going to the landfill, they can be placed elsewhere on the site to replenish soil nutrients and provide habitat for ground-loving creatures. When native plants reseed and "volunteers" appear on your site, encourage diversity by letting some of them remain, or transplant some to other locations on the site.

Try not to prune excessively. Pruning removes wildlife food and cover. In some areas of the site, encourage variety and diversity in the structure of plants by letting dead branches remain on shrub and small trees.

Make an effort to minimize and eventually eliminate the use of chemical pesticides. Their killing is not limited to the insects you want to remove. Several effective biological controls are available. See Appendix 1 for information.

Adapted from Nordstrom, Sue and Margy Halpin, Creating Landscapes for Wildlife: A Guide for Backyards in Utah.

Plan for the maintenance of all components of your plan in general for 5-10 years, and in detail for at least one year. The detailed one-year plan will include a maintenance schedule.

MAINTENANCE SCHEDULE

A maintenance schedule will increase your chances of success and ensure that your wildlife project remains healthy and productive. Post a copy in a public place, so everyone on your team will know what needs to be done, when it needs to be done, and who is expected to do it.

The custodial staff and school administrator should have a copy of this schedule, since they will most likely be involved in the maintenance process. During the summer months while students are out of school, you'll need to work closely with the school maintenance staff. Students and teachers who live nearby may also choose to be involved.

An effective maintenance schedule includes:

1. calendars - seasonal, monthly, even weekly, tasks, written as specifically as possible so someone new to the project could do them
2. the name of the person or group responsible for completing the task; include a space for initialing when the task is completed

A maintenance schedule worksheet is included in Appendix J.

Here is an example of the monthly tasks that might be included in a maintenance schedule for a calendar year.

Overview of Monthly Maintenance Tasks

January
Keep all bird feeders clean and filled.

February
Clean old nests from bird nest boxes.
Keep all bird feeders clean and filled.
Put up new bird nesting boxes.
Pull up frost-killed annuals from herb garden and horticulture plot.

March
Check all structures for winter damage.
Check around pond for damage or areas where liner is exposed.
Keep all bird feeders clean and filled.
Check nesting boxes once a week.

April
Reinstall pump in pond.
Clean up leaf litter and dead plants in plant beds.
Till perch n' plant, horticulture plot, and other areas as needed.
Keep all bird feeders clean and filled.
Check nesting boxes at least once a week.

May
Plant wildlife foods plot, and other herbaceous wildlife cover.
Plant horticulture and other plots.
Keep bird feeders clean and filled.
Check nesting boxes at least once a week.

June
Weed horticulture and other plots.
Bring in bird feeders, clean thoroughly and store.
Clearly mark areas that should not be mowed during the summer.
If pond cannot be supervised, remove pump and return animals
to proper habitat; drain pond.

July
Weed horticulture and other plots.
Repaint, restain or repair all wooden structures as needed.

August
Weed horticulture and other plots.

September
Set out insect traps.
Weed horticulture and other plots.
Re-establish pond.

October
Order trees for next spring.
Thin bulbs, corms and tubers.
Take down insect traps.
Cover pond with wire mesh or netting to keep leaves out.
Begin filling bird feeders.

November
Remove pump from pond.
Mow wildflower plot.
Clean out nesting boxes.
Prune deciduous trees and shrubs.
Keep bird feeders clean and filled.

December
Keep all bird feeders clean and filled.
Prune deciduous trees and shrubs.

"Don't panic...slow down...
everything doesn't have to be
completed now...think long
term and enjoy the power of
discovery."

BIANCA MCRAE
RAYMOND SCHOOL
RAYMOND, NH

Ongoing general maintenance as needed:
> trail construction and repair; turn compost pile; mow grass; check water level in small ponds and add water as needed.

(Excerpted with permission from: <u>So You Want to Start An Outdoor Classroom...</u> Compiled and edited by: OK Conservation Commission and OK Department of Wildlife Conservation, and <u>Guidelines and Features for Outdoor Classrooms</u>, Indiana Department of Natural Resources, Division of Forestry)

Maintenance Specifics and Suggestions

To determine the maintenance needs of particular projects, see Chapter 6. For example, bird feeders will need to be filled daily, garden plots weeded regularly, plantings pruned seasonally, and nest boxes cleaned annually.

THE OUTDOOR CLASSROOM

Once the components of the project are in place, you may think your work is done, but your involvement and activity don't stop here! By working on this wildlife enhancement project, you have been creating an outdoor classroom.

There are a wealth of possibilities for continued study, experience, and learning in the outdoors, including future projects to benefit wildlife. This can readily become part of the regular curriculum at your school.

In addition, maintaining the project through the seasons will serve to inspire new outdoor study ideas. Establishing a log book, collecting, observing, and evaluating, will all contribute to the development of this experience and act as a springboard into new ones.

Start from What You Know

To begin this process, consider the following questions. Include the students in exploring the answers. With the familiarity and understanding your team has gained of your schoolyard site, this shouldn't be too difficult.

- What features exist on the site that could serve as focal points for environmental studies?

- What natural ecological processes might be demonstrated using features of the site (i.e. change, succession, interdependence, interrelationships, adaptations, etc.)?

- What negative or unfavorable environmental factors exist on the outdoor school site which might be studied, analyzed, and remedied as part of the educational process at the school?

- What evidence can you find of positive environmental attitudes of students toward the outdoor school site? What evidence of negative environmental attitudes?

- What interesting historical features exist on the site? How do you think that such features might be woven into some sort of environmental interpretation in the school curriculum?

- Suggest an outdoor activity that might be carried out in each of the following curriculum areas:
  Fine Arts, Language Arts, Math, Music, Science, Social Studies

(Excerpted from Jerry Schierloh, Assoc. Prof. of Envtl. Studies, NJ School of Conservation, Documents from Graduate Course: "Outdoor Teaching Sites for Environmental Education", Montclair State College.)

To guide you in this effort, we've collected a sampler of activities from some of our favorite program guides and reprinted them in Appendix K. Like the project itself, these are multidisciplinary, interdisciplinary activities that can be done with different grade levels in the elementary school. You, as the teacher, can create a sequence of activities for your students to follow, based on your objectives and integrated with your classroom curriculum.

All of these guides are also listed in the Instructional Resources, Appendix H, under "Activities," with information on how you can acquire a copy.

✎ Outdoor Study Ideas

The activities suggested here are just a few of the things you can do to learn more about wildlife and increase your skills and appreciation.

- Sketch, paint or draw an animal. Study the work of wildlife artists.

- Learn to identify the sounds of various animals. (Recordings are available to help you do this.) Use a tape recorder to record sounds you hear.

- Do a focused census of the entire plant and/or animal population on a few square feet of your site. Note which species are native and which were introduced from other parts of the world (exotic).

- Choose a spot, such as a pond or a lone tree in a field, and observe and record its use by animals. Construct a food web based on your observation.

- Collect, identify, and press (preserve) plants from a certain habitat. Mount and display them with information on each plant's value to wildlife.

- Learn to identify five birds. Then repeat for mammals, fish, reptiles, insects, etc. Don't learn just from books. Observe in the field, noting habitat, flight or running pattern, and other distinguishing characteristics.

- Observe (with binoculars) parent birds carrying food to young in a nest. Record the number of trips per hour and kinds of food. Estimate the total amount of various types of food the nestlings eat each day.

- Raise wildlife shrubs from seeds or cuttings. Write a habitat improvement leaflet, and give it and a bundle of shrubs to people in your area who agree to plant them.

- Put different kinds of feed in similar feeders, and determine food preferences of different bird species. Compare your findings to their natural diet. Do this for ants, chipmunks, raccoons, caterpillars, or other wild creatures.

- Locate a nest being built by a bird, perhaps in one of your nest boxes. Observe it closely during the nesting season. Determine average distance traveled per trip. Calculate total distance traveled to build the nest. Keep detailed records of activity. Include number of trips per hour when building, behavior when other birds, cats, etc. are nearby, number of eggs when laid, hatching date, etc. Compare your observations to information published on that species in books.

(Excerpted with permission from Environmental Awareness: Wildlife, *Otis F. Curtis, University of Connecticut, Cooperative Extension System.)*

✍ MAINTENANCE GENERATES NEW STUDY

Maintenance will become a project for study in itself. A carefully kept and well-detailed record of your project will serve as an excellent tool for evaluating the success of your project. This could include photographs or slides, video, maps (with new mapping projects every year), a log book, plantings growth charts, and wildlife sightings charts. Keep this record in a central location, such as the school library, for all team members to use.

In addition, maintaining the project through the seasons will serve to inspire new outdoor study ideas. Consider these possibilities:

- Highlight your project with a sign to attract community attention and appreciation and divert vandalism.

- Organize a campaign to advertise your project.

- Have your team do a presentation for a community organization on the project. Include the theories behind the various activities.

"Right now my students are thinking about their own little habitat video to send to other schools."

PAUL OUIMET, S.T.E.P.,
WHITE MOUNTAIN
REGIONAL HIGH SCHOOL
WHITEFIELD, NH

- Maintain a scrapbook of newspaper and other articles about your site.
- Adopt a park or nearby conservation area for further study if your site is small.

Education Comfort Zone

Have your class establish a comfort zone for wildlife around their project area. This will be a "no trespassing observation area" between the project and curious humans. It will keep disturbance or harassment of wildlife to a minimum. Your students can organize a school awareness program to explain their venture and why visiting wildlife should be left alone.

Comfort zones are also ideal for teaching purposes. Students can use them to observe, identify, report and explain why certain species are attracted to the area.

In addition, an established foot trail is a good way to prevent students from trampling over tree seedlings, ground nesting animals and vegetation with low tolerance for foot traffic. For planning a trail system, topography, soils types, drainage, vegetation and obstacles are some factors to consider, as well as routing the trail to all points of interest.

Material for this chapter excerpted or adapted with permission from:

Environmental Awareness: Wildlife, Otis F. Curtis, University of Connecticut, Cooperative Extension System

Guidelines and Features for Outdoor Classrooms, Indiana Department of Natural Resources, Division of Forestry

Nordstrom, Sue and Margy Halpin. *Creating Landscapes for Wildlife: A Guide for Backyards in Utah,* Department of Landscape Architecture and Environmental Planning, Utah State University, and Utah Division of Wildlife Resources, 1991

So You Want to Start An Outdoor Classroom... Compiled and edited by: OK Conservation Commission and OK Department of Wildlife Conservation

Jerry Schierloh, Assoc. Prof. of Envtl. Studies, NJ School of Conservation, Documents from Graduate Course: "Outdoor Teaching Sites for Environmental Education," Montclair State College.

Epilogue
Habitat for the Future

Wildlife benefits from direct enhancement of the habitat. In addition, wildlife benefits from the lifelong awareness and concern that is fostered in the learners.

INTO THE FUTURE

Enhancing habitats for wildlife brings community attention to the quality of vegetation, water sources, soil and air. These elements of life support are necessary to provide food, water, shelter, and space suitably arranged for wildlife.

What's good for wildlife tends to be good for people too. As these sites mature through the years, they can leave a lasting contribution to the quality of life.

Keeping the Project Alive

The biggest challenge, once a schoolyard habitat enhancement project has been established, is to sustain it. That is also one of the most important concerns. Taking responsibility to benefit the environment is not something we do once and then forget about. It is a lifetime commitment. A habitat enhancement project offers the place and the opportunity to learn about making that commitment and to sustain it over time.

"There are some who can live without wild things, and some who cannot...Like winds and sunsets, wild things were taken for granted until progress began to do away with them. Now we face the question whether a still higher 'standard of living' is worth its cost in things natural, wild, and free. For us of the minority, the opportunity to see geese is more important than television, and the chance to find a pasque-flower is a right as inalienable as free speech."

Aldo Leopold, A Sand County Almanac

Material for this epilogue adapted with permission from:

WILD School Sites: A Guide to Preparing for Habitat Improvement Projects on School Grounds, Western Regional Environmental Education Council, 1993

Section V

Appendices

"The first rule of intelligent tinkering is to save all the pieces."

Aldo Leopold, The Land Ethic

Appendix A
Glossary

adapted, adaptation: the process of making adjustments to the environment.

annual: when referring to plants, those that complete their life cycle from seed to mature seed-bearing plant in one growing season.

aquatic: growing in, living in, or frequenting water.

broadleaf: a plant with wide blade leaves, such as an oak. Seeds are borne from flowering parts in contrast to conifers which bear seeds in cones.

browse: a general term, commonly used in wildlife management to signify brushy plants utilized by deer, elk or cattle as feed; to eat the twigs and leaves of woody plants.

canopy: the more or less continuous cover of branches and foliage formed by the collective crowns of trees, shrubs, weeds, and grasses.

carrying capacity: The maximum number of animals that can be sustained on an area of land over a period of time. Carrying capacity varies throughout the year.

climax: the final stage of plant or animal succession; when environmental conditions have been stable long enough for an area to develop a semi-permanent biome.

competition: when two or more organisms use the same resource.

conifer: usually refers to needleleaf trees that bear their seeds in cones. Spruces, pines, and firs are examples.

conservation: wise use of the environment that results in the greatest good for the greatest number of people and wildlife species for the greatest length of time.

corridor: areas of continuous habitat that permit animals to travel securely from one habitat to another. Corridors allow wildlife to find islands of habitat that have been created by fragmentation.

cover: vegetation and other land features that provide areas for wildlife to hide, sleep, feed, and reproduce. Also called shelter.

deciduous: plants that shed their foliage at the end of the growing season. Usually trees and shrubs.

diversity: the condition of being varied, of having many parts. In a habitat, diversity means the presence of many forms of wildlife and plant use.

dominant: the plant or animal species that is the most noticeable and common in an area. Often is a controlling force in the community where it occurs.

ecosystem: an interacting natural system including all the biological organisms and the nonliving components of the environment, including climate and geology.

edge: the zone where plant communities meet or where successional stages or vegetative conditions within plant communities come together.

evergreen: plants that do not lose all their leaves at one time. Usually conifer trees, but also some broadleaf trees such as live oak.

exotic: in conservation language, this refers to a foreign plant or animal — one that that evolved in another region or another continent and has been introduced into a new area.

forb: low growing herbaceous plants, both annuals and perennials.

food chain: the path through which energy is transferred from plants to herbivores (plant eaters) and then to carnivores (meat eaters).

forage: refers to the vegetation eaten by animals.

habitat: any area which fulfills the four basic needs — food, water, cover, space — of any particular species in a suitable arrangement.

hardwood: a type of tree with broad leaves, not needles.

hardiness zone: a horticultural zone which refers to the northern-most areas in which a plant species can be expected to be winter hardy.

herb: plant, often aromatic, that has medicinal value or is used for food seasoning.

herbaceous: all grasses and forbs having soft rather than woody stems, including flowers and plants called weeds. Above-ground portions of perennial herbaceous plants die back each year and are replaced by new growth.

interspersion: the mix of plant species and plant communities that provides habitat for animals in a defined area.

legume: a plant which bears its seeds in pods that split into two halves with seeds attached to the lower edge of one of the halves. Legume roots typically have nodules in which atmospheric nitrogen can be transformed into soluble nitrogen usable by plants.

limiting factor: the habitat need that is in shortest supply and, therefore, prevents the wildlife population from getting larger. Limiting factors interact to define the carrying capacity.

management: the intentional manipulation or non-manipulation of habitat and/or the organisms within the habitat.

mast: nuts or acorns.

microclimate: the climate of a specific small area. Microclimates are the tiny contrasts to the general climate of the area. The shady side of a huge boulder or the north side of a city building would be classified as microclimates.

migratory: in wildlife usage, birds or other animals which make annual migrations, i.e., travel distances in seasonal movements.

monoculture: cultivation of a single crop to the exclusion of other plants.

native plants: a plant species that originally occurred in an area.

old growth: a forest stand which has aged to 1.5 times the age at which the timber is normally harvested.

perennial: a plant that lives for several years.

population: the number of a particular species in a defined area.

population dynamics: the study of forces and influences which cause change in the increase and decrease of wildlife populations.

predator: an animal that captures, kills, and eats prey.

prey: an animal that is caught, killed, and eaten by predators.

shelter: a place where an animal can hide from predators or the weather to sleep, rest, or raise its young.

shrub: plants with woody stems that are usually less than 12 feet tall. Often have many main stems rather than one main stem (trunk).

snag: a standing, dead tree.

softwood: usually refers to coniferous trees. Some deciduous trees, such as aspen, also have relatively soft wood.

species: animals and plants that are the same and successfully reproduce the same kind of plant or animal.

structural habitat components: nest boxes and nest platforms, dust and grit, cut banks, cliffs and caves, dens, snags, downed logs and perches, water, salt and other trace minerals, feeders, rock piles, and brush piles that are used by wildlife.

succession: the orderly, gradual, and continuous replacement of one plant or animal species by another.

topography: the relief or lay of the land, including surface configuration, contours, slopes, and drainage patterns. *tree:* a plant that is usually more than 12 feet tall and has a single main woody stem with a distinct crown of leaves.

urban wildlife: mammals, birds, and fish that have adapted to life in developed areas. Urban wildlife includes all those species that live in cities and suburbs.

understory: the layer of plants growing under another higher layer of plants, e.g., grass, weeds and brush under forest trees.

vegetation: the mass of plants that covers a given area.

vegetative habitat components: plants that are used by wildlife, including living conifers, legumes, butterfly, bee, and moth plants, hummingbird plants, spring plants, summer plants, fall plants, winter plants, and mast-producing plants.

vertical structure: also called "layering," refers to how different layers of vegetation are arranged in relation to each other, including the ground layer, shrub layer, and tree canopy. Different wildlife species utilize different layers to meet their habitat needs.

watershed: the entire region of land draining into a river, river system, or body of water. Also called a drainage basin.

wetlands: lands which contain much soil moisture. Wetlands include tidal flats, swamps, marshes, bogs, fens, wet meadows, and bottom lands. Wetlands are one of the most endangered natural resources.

wildlife: native wild animals, including birds, mammals, reptiles, amphibians, fish and invertebrates, which don't depend on humans to meet their basic survival needs.

wildlife management: the application of scientific knowledge and technical skills to protect, preserve, conserve, limit, enhance, or extend the value of wildlife and its habitat.

Material for this glossary excerpted or adapted from:

Neilson, Edward Jr., and Delwin Benson, 1991, *4-H Wildlife Habitat Evaluation Handbook*, National 4-H Council, MD

Developed Lands Kit, National Institute for Urban Wildlife, 10921 Trotting Ridge Way, Columbia, MD 21044

Henderson, Carrol L. 1987. *Landscaping for Wildlife*. MN Dept. of Nat. Res., St. Paul, address

Project WILD Activity Guide, Western Regional Environmental Education Council, second edition, 1992

Appendix B
Sample Maps

The maps in this appendix show the site of the New Hampshire Fish & Game Twin Mountain Fish Hatchery, located in Carroll, NH. They represent the various types of maps and related information you can access to produce a base map for your site. These include: USGS Topographic Map, SCS Soils Survey Map, Tax Map, Site Plot, and Aerial Photograph.

Refer to Chapter 3 for a discussion of mapping. Refer to Appendix G for information on agencies providing these maps.

USGS Topographic Map

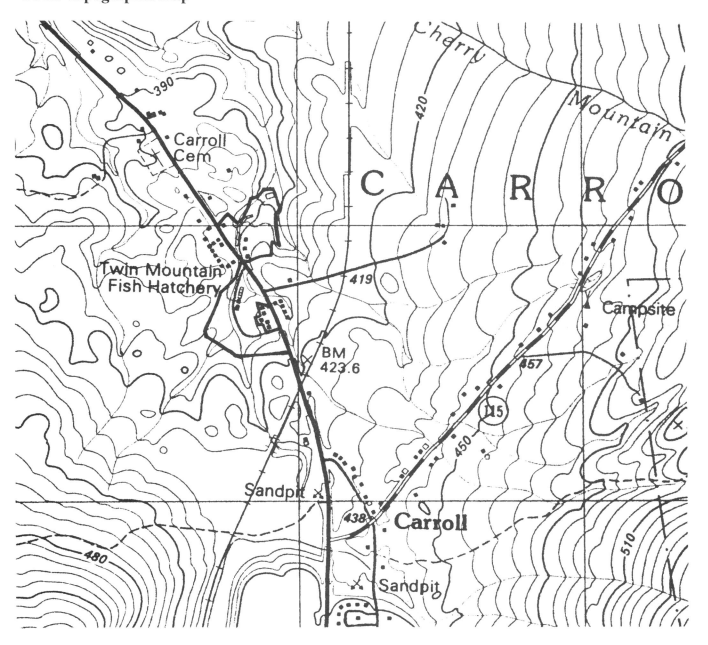

Site Plot

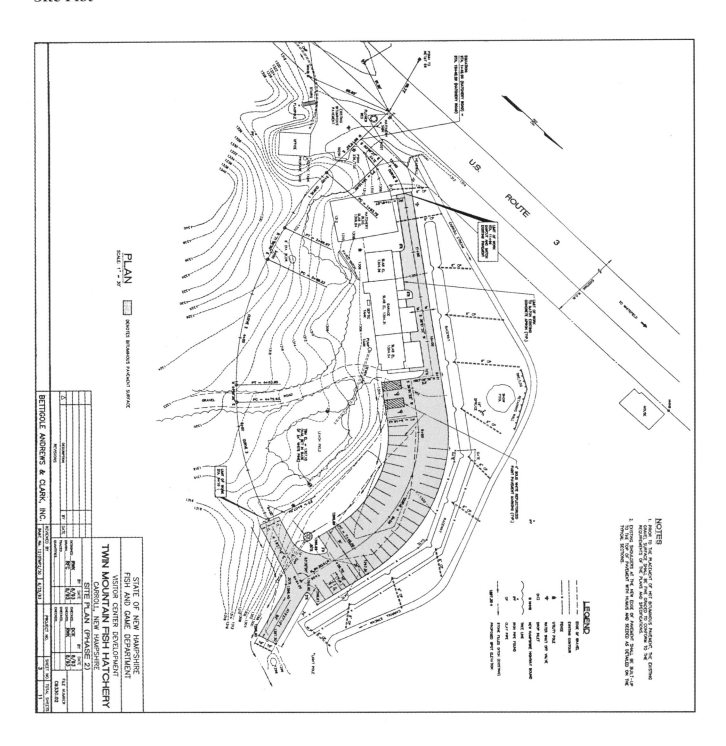

Tax Map

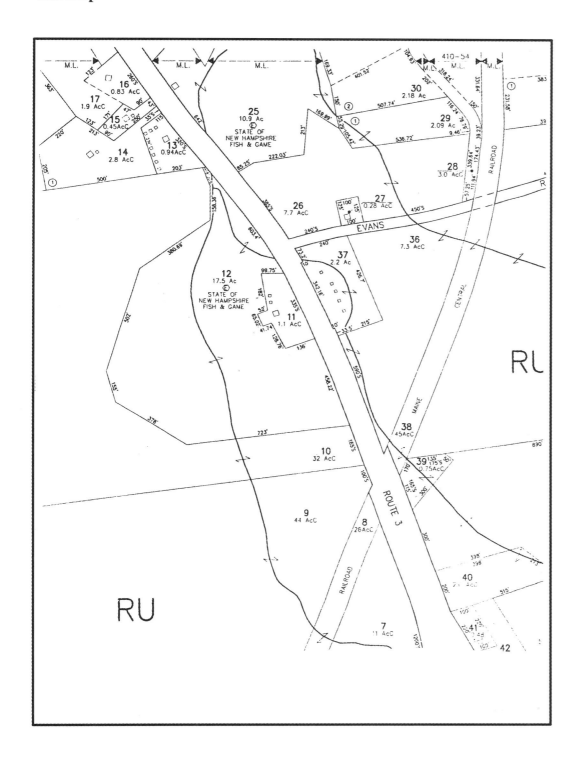

Soils Survey Map

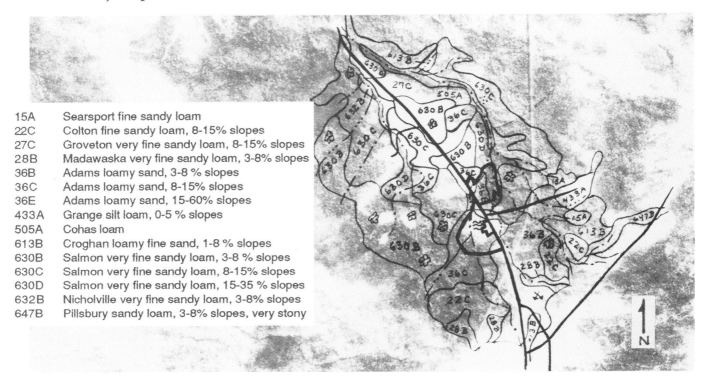

15A	Searsport fine sandy loam
22C	Colton fine sandy loam, 8-15% slopes
27C	Groveton very fine sandy loam, 8-15% slopes
28B	Madawaska very fine sandy loam, 3-8% slopes
36B	Adams loamy sand, 3-8 % slopes
36C	Adams loamy sand, 8-15% slopes
36E	Adams loamy sand, 15-60% slopes
433A	Grange silt loam, 0-5 % slopes
505A	Cohas loam
613B	Croghan loamy fine sand, 1-8 % slopes
630B	Salmon very fine sandy loam, 3-8 % slopes
630C	Salmon very fine sandy loam, 8-15% slopes
630D	Salmon very fine sandy loam, 15-35 % slopes
632B	Nicholville very fine sandy loam, 3-8% slopes
647B	Pillsbury sandy loam, 3-8% slopes, very stony

Aerial Photograph

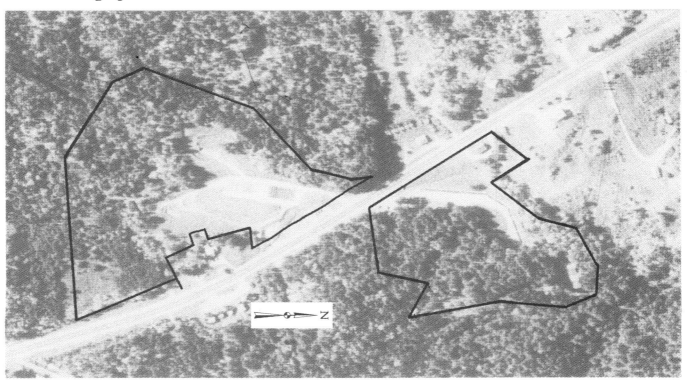

Appendix C
New England Habitat Types and Associated Wildlife

HABITAT TYPES

As you conduct an inventory of your schoolyard site, you will find that certain plant species are dominant in the area. These plants are able to survive and thrive in your schoolyard due to a number of factors, including soils type, climate, rainfall, and elevation. Habitat types are classified by the dominant plant species that occur in a particular area.

HABITAT KEY

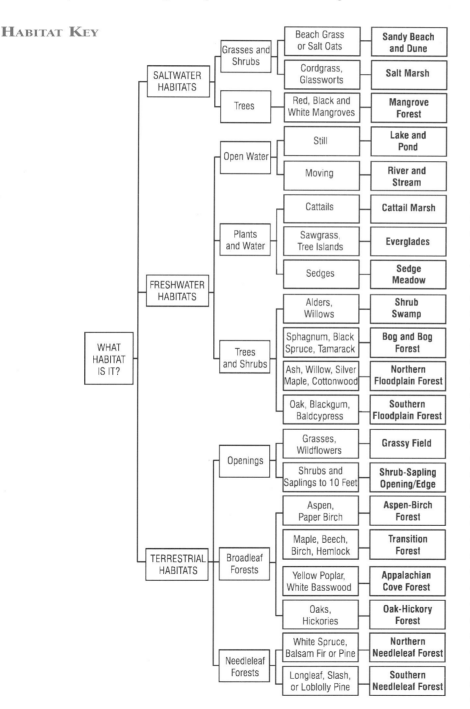

(Reprinted with permission from Janine Benyus, The Field Guide to Habitats of the Eastern United States, Fireside Books, Simon and Schuster, Inc., NY, 1989. Also available, by the same author, The Field Guide to Habitats of the Western United States.)

Wildlife species will be found in areas of specific habitat types, utilizing the components of food, water, and cover provided by those particular plants and their associated habitat. For instance, porcupines, who prefer to eat the sweet inner bark of conifers, are attracted to spruce/fir forests. Wild turkeys enjoy the mast (acorns and nuts) and low, shrubby cover provided by the oak/hickory forest.

We've chosen three commonly occurring types to describe here: Northern Hardwoods, Spruce/Fir, and White Pine/Red Oak. As part of your inventory, you will want to do some further research into the habitat type(s) that surround your school. For this purpose, we recommend two resources. The following descriptions of forest cover types have been excerpted from *New England Wildlife: Habitat, Natural History, and Distribution,* by DeGraaf and Rudis. (Copies may be available from your local library, Cooperative Extension office, regional biologist, or forest service. See the Instructional Resources, Appendix H, list for information on how to acquire a copy.) This invaluable resource also discusses habitat types that occur in nonforested areas (like fields) and wetlands areas (such as lakes). *The Field Guide to Wildlife Habitats of the Eastern United States,* and its companion volume for the Western United States, by Janine M. Benyus, provide a readable discussion of habitat and profiles of the different types with their associated wildlife species.

FOREST COVER TYPES AND GROUPS

Northern Hardwoods
(including sugar maple, sugar maple/beech/yellow birch, and beech/sugar maple)

True northern hardwoods are dominated by sugar maple (Acer saccharum), beech (Fagus grandifolia), and yellow birch (Betula lutea) and occur widely as a pure type in northern New England. It grades into a mixed hardwood or transition type in southern New England. Associated species throughout the region include basswood (Tilia americana), red maple (Acer rubrum), hemlock (Tsuga canadensis), white ash (Fraxinus americana), white pine (Pinus strobus), balsam fir (Abies balsamea), black cherry (Prunus serotina), paper birch (Betula papyrifera), sweet birch (Betula lenta), and red spruce (Picea rubens).

Northern hardwood is the basic hardwood type in northern New England, and occurs to an elevation of 2,500 feet (760 m.). It prefers fertile loamy soils and good moisture conditions. Striped maple (Acer pensylvanicum), witch-hazel (Hamamelis virginiana), and hobblebush (Viburnum alnifolium) are common in the understory throughout the region. Best development of the type occurs on moist fertile, well-drained loamy soils.

On drier sites, beech becomes more predominant. On wet sites, the type blends into a red/yellow birch/hemlock or red spruce mixture. This tends to be a climax type woodlands. (Berglund 1980)

Associated wildlife species:

  Mammals: white-tailed deer, eastern chipmunk
  Birds: eastern bluebird, wood duck, wild turkey
  Herptiles: spotted salamander

White Pine/Northern Red Oak/Red Maple

Northern red oak (Quercus rubra), Eastern white pine (Pinus strobus), and red maple predominate; white ash is the most common associate, but others include paper birch, yellow birch (B. alleghaniensis), and sweet birch (B. Lenta), sugar maple, beech, hemlock, and black cherry. Occurs across southern and central New England to an elevation of 1,500 feet (450 m), and generally on deep, well-drained fertile soils.

This type is common in the transition between northern hardwoods and spruce-fir types in northern New England, and between northern hardwoods and oak types — characteristic of central types — in southern New England. The type often follows "old field" white pine in New England, where hardwood seedlings and saplings form the understory (Baldwin and Ward 1980). Common understory shrubs include witch-hazel, alternate-leaf dogwood (Cornus alternifolia), mapleleaf viburnum (Viburnum acerifolium), and mountain-laurel (Kalmia latifolia).

Associated wildlife species:

  Mammals: red fox, grey fox, white-footed mouse, gray squirrel
  Birds: pileated woodpecker, barred owl
  Herptiles: wood turtle, redback salamander

Red Spruce/Balsam Fir

The type may consist of red spruce and balsam fir or together they may predominate in a mixture of associates; the composition varies by site and disturbance history. This is a northern New England type, occupying moderately to poorly drained flats, but not swamps. Associates are red maple, paper and yellow birch, aspens, primarily, but also white pine, hemlock, and occasionally black spruce (Picea mariana) and tamarack (Larix laricina).

The type occurs near sea level in eastern Maine, from an elevation of 2,400 to 4,500 feet in the White Mountains of New Hampshire, from an elevation of 2,500 to 3,800 feet in the Green Mountains of Vermont, and occurs on the tops of some of the higher Berkshire Hills in western Massachusetts.

The type occurs on two kinds of sites in New England: 1) poorly drained flats and ridges or benches at lake shores, streams, and swamps and bogs,

and 2) well-drained to dry, shallow, soils on steep, rocky, upper mountain slopes.

Associated wildlife species:

    Mammals: fisher, porcupine, red squirrel, snowshoe hare
    Birds: dark-eyed junco, pine siskin, redbreasted nuthatch
    Herptiles: redbelly snake

Appendix D
Wildlife Food Charts

COMMON WILDLIFE FOODS

WILDLIFE GROUPS / **FOOD GROUPS**

FROGS	SALAMANDERS	TURTLES	OTTER	BATS	RACCOON	WOODPECKERS	SNAKES	SHREWS	OWLS	BEAVER	FOXES	HAWKS	WOOD DUCK	BLUEBIRD	QUAIL	RABBIT	SQUIRREL	DEER	TURKEY	FOOD GROUP
×		×			×	×							×		×				×	SPIDERS
					×	×							×				×	×	×	ACORNS
					×								×				×		×	NUTS
																	×	×		MUSHROOMS
					×	×					×	×	×				×		×	MISC. SEEDS
		×			×	×				×	×	×	×	×	×	×	×	×	×	FRUIT
					×														×	TUBERS
		×			×					×					×	×		×	×	GREENS
×	×	×		×	×	×	×	×	×		×	×	×	×	×				×	INSECTS
×	×				×	×		×					×	×	×				×	SNAILS
										×							×	×	×	LEAVES, TWIGS
																		×		LICHENS
																		×		FERNS
																×	×	×		BUDS
					×								×		×	×	×	×	×	GRAIN
										×						×				BARK
		×	×		×	×	×		×			×	×							FISH
×			×		×		×	×				×	×							FROGS & SALAMANDERS
×			×				×		×				×							SNAKES
×		×	×		×							×	×						×	CRAYFISH
			×		×		×		×				×							BIRDS
			×		×		×	×	×		×	×								SM. MAMMALS
		×									×		×							AQUATIC PLANTS
		×								×										CARION
×	×				×		×	×			×									EARTHWORMS
	×				×		×													EGGS
		×	×		×								×							MUSSELS

SOURCE: Delwin Benson and Edward Neilson, *Wildlife Habitat Evaluation Handbook*, National 4-H Council, Chevy Chase, MD, 1991.

WOODY PLANTS OF NEW ENGLAND

Principal Reference: *American Wildlife and Plants*, by Martin, Zim, and Nelson (McGraw-Hill, 1951)

KEY

Number Rating	Approximate percent of diet seasonally
1	1/2 to under 2
2	2 to under 5
3	5 to under 10
4	10 to under 25
5	25 to under 50
6	50 and over

Plant	Woodpecker, Pileated	Woodpecker, Hairy	Woodpecker, Downy	Waxwing, Cedar	Warbler, Pine	Vireo, Red-eyed	Towhee, Eastern	Titmouse, Tufted	Thrush, Wood	Thrush, Veery	Thrush, Hermit	Thrasher, Brown	Tanager, Scarlet	Swallow, Tree	Starling	Sparrow, White-throated	Sparrow, Fox	Siskin, Pine	Sapsucker, Yellow-bellied	Robin	Redpoll, Common	Phoebe	Oriole, Northern	Nuthatch, White-breasted	Nuthatch, Red-breasted	Mockingbird	Kingbird	Jay, Blue	Grosbeak, Rose-breasted	Grosbeak, Evening	Goldfinch, Common	Grackle, Common	Flicker, Yellow-shafted	Finch, Purple	Crow, Fish	Crow, Common
Oaks (*Quercus*)			1					3	3			2			1				2						4			5	1			3	1			2
Blackberries (*Rubus*)				2		2	3	2	2	2		3	2		1		3			2		1	2		2	2	1	1	2	1	4	2	1		3	1
Cherries (*Prunus*)			1	4		2	1	3	1	2	1	3	1			3	1			4		1	2			1	2	1	3	4	5		2	3		2
Dogwoods (*Cornus*)	1	1	2	3	2	2			3	3		2	1		1	1	2						3		1	2	2	1		5	2		1			1
Grapes (*Vitis*)	3		2	1		2	1	1	2	2		2	2			2	2			2					2	2							1	1	1	1
Pines (*Pinus*)					3			2					1					3		2				2	2	5				1						
Blueberries (*Vaccinium*)								2	1	2		2			1					1		1	2		2	1			1	1				1		
Maples (*Acer*)																				2				2					1	5	1	2				
Sumas (*Rhus*)					1					1		2	1		3					3			2		2					1			1	1		1
Beech (*Fagus*)												3								2				1				2	2			1	1			
Mulberries (*Morus*)				2								1	1		2					1			2		2	2						1		3		2
Birches (*Betula*)																2		4	2		4												1			
Elderberries (*Sambucus*)					1	1		1	1	2	2	2	2		2	2	1			1		1			2	2	1			3						
Serviceberries (*Amalanchier*)		1	1	2			2	2	2	2		2								2			2			1	1						1	1		1
Blackgum (*Nyssa*)	3	1	1	1		1			2	2		2			2					3				2		2							2	1		
Greenbriers (*Smilax*)	1		1	1						2		2				1				1				3		3					5		1			1
Poison Ivy (*Toxicodendron*)	1	2	3		2				1						2	2	2					1								4			1			1
Cedars (*Juniperus*)				5						1	1				2	2				2					2	2				2			1	3		1
Virginia Creepers (*Parthenocissus*)	2	1	1		2								2			1				2			2			3				2			1			1
Spruces (*Picea*)																				2					2											
Aspens (*Populus*)																																				
Hazelnuts (*Corylus*)																																				
Hickories (*Carya*)																				2						1			2		2					
Hollies (*Ilex*)	2				1						1	3								2	1	1		2		3							1			
Ashes (*Fraxinus*)				1																				2						1				2		
Elms (*Ulmus*)																								2					1	2				4		
Willows (*Salix*)																																				
Hemlock (*Tsuga*)																		4																		
Firs (*Abies*)																				2																
Hawthorns (*Crataegus*)																	4					1														
Alders (*Alnus*)														1							4										2					
Mountain Ashes (*Sorbus*)																															2					
Tuliptree (*Liriodendron*)																		2												1				3		
Walnuts (*Juglans*)																																				

AND THEIR FOOD VALUE FOR WILDLIFE

KEY

Number Rating	Approximate percent of diet seasonally
1	1/2 to under 2
2	2 to under 5
3	5 to under 10
4	10 to under 25
5	25 to under 50
6	50 and over

Species	Crossbill, Red	Chickadee, Black-capped	Catbird	Cardinal	Bluebird	OTHER BIRDS	Turkey	Quail, Bobwhite	Pheasant, Ring-necked	Grouse, Ruffed	Duck, Wood	Duck, Mallard	GAME BIRDS	Squirrel Flying	Porcupine	Mouse, White-Footed	Mouse, Meadow	Chipmunk, Eastern	OTHER MAMMALS	Squirrel, Red	Squirrel, Gray	Skunk, Striped	Raccoon	Rabbit, Cottontail, New England	Rabbit, Cottontail, Eastern	Opossum	Moose	Hare, Snowshoe	Fox, Red	Fox, Gray	Deer, White-Tailed	Beaver	Bear, Black
Oaks (*Quercus*)							5	2	2	3	2	2		3	2	3	2	3		3	5		5	1		1		1			4		5
Blackberries (*Rubus*)			4	1	1		2	2	4	3								2			1			3		1		1	1		3		
Cherries (*Prunus*)			3		1					3	3					2		2		2	1	1		2	2			2	1		2		5
Dogwoods (*Cornus*)			2	3	2		2	1		3	4					1		2						2		3		3	1		2		
Grapes (*Vitis*)			2	4			4	2		3	2											3	2			2			1	1			3
Pines (*Pinus*)	6	3												3	2					2	2						1	5			1		
Blueberries (*Vaccinium*)			2				2			3						3						2	2					1			3		4
Maples (*Acer*)									2					2	4	2	2	3		3	3		2				2	1			4	2	
Sumacs (*Rhus*)			2	2	2			2		2										3		5				1		2			2		
Beech (*Fagus*)										3	2			4	4			3		3	3		1					1					5
Mulberries (*Morus*)			1	2																	2					2							
Birches (*Betula*)		2								3				3									2				3	3			2	3	
Elderberries (*Sambucus*)			2		1				2	2								2															
Serviceberries (*Amalanchier*)			2	1	1					2												3						2			1	3	
Blackgum (*Nyssa*)									1												2										3	3	
Greenbriers (*Smilax*)			2						1	2													1				1				3	2	
Poison Ivy (*Toxicodendron*)		2		1			1	2																									
Cedars (*Juniperus*)				1	2													2													1	1	1
Virginia Creepers (*Parthenocissus*)				1	2																												
Spruces (*Picea*)	2																	3		3	2							4					
Aspens (*Populus*)											5				2		2										3	3			3	4	
Hazelnuts (*Corylus*)										3								3		2							1	2			1	3	
Hickories (*Carya*)																		3		4	4						1						
Hollies (*Ilex*)			1																								1				2	1	
Ashes (*Fraxinus*)				1			1	2			1				2													1			2	2	
Elms (*Ulmus*)										3										3	1							1					
Willows (*Salix*)										3							2										4	4			2	3	
Hemlock (*Tsuga*)	2	2													4																3		
Firs (*Abies*)	1	2													3						2							4			2		
Hawthorns (*Crataegus*)										3												1									1	1	3
Alders (*Alnus*)																											2	2			2	2	
Mountain Ashes (*Sorbus*)																												4					
Tuliptree (*Liriodendron*)				2												2					2						2	1			2		
Walnuts (*Juglans*)																				2	2												

Appendix E
Planting Charts and Plant Care

Following is a list of valuable wildlife plantings that grow well throughout much of New England. These plantings will greatly enhance food and cover conditions in the typical lawn and landscaped shrub setting found in the immediate schoolyard area.

Always inventory the area first to make sure you are not planting something that is already abundant on your site. If in doubt about a particular plant's ability to grow in your area, check with your county cooperative extension program or a local nursery.

Some of the plants listed, such as barberry and autumn olive, are not native to New England. They can be invasive in open field situations and should only be planted if a careful maintenance schedule is in place to keep them in check.

Remember, the selections of the plants is only one step. Careful arrangement of them when planting is crucial to their value, creating a good diversity of high and low plantings and interspersion of food and cover plants. Refer to Chapter 2 for a discussion of these concepts, and consult the books listed in Appendix H for suggested arrangements of plantings.

Woody Plants and Vines

common name(s) scientific name	soil moisture (wet to dry)	light tolerance (sun to shade)	flowering dates	fruit/seeds available	ornamental value	native
Tall Trees						
Eastern white pine *Pinus strobus*	moist/dry	sun	—	Aug-Sept	excellent	yes
Eastern red cedar *Juniperus virginiana*	moist/dry	sun	—	Sept-May	excellent	yes
Black cherry *Prunus serotina*	moist/dry	sun	—	Aug-Oct	good	yes
White oak *Quercus alba*	moist/dry	sun/lt shade	—	Sept-Nov	excellent	yes
Red oak *Quercus rubra*	moist	sun/lt shade	—	Sept-Oct	excellent	yes
Spruce *Picea spp.*	moist/ well-drained	sun/lt shade	—	Aug-Sept	good-excellent	some
N. white cedar or arborvitae *Thuja occidentalis*	wet/dry	sun/shade	—	Sept-Nov	excellent	yes
Eastern hemlock *Tsuga canadensis*	moist/dry	sun/shade	—	Aug-Sept	good-excellent	yes
Medium-small Trees						
Chokecherry* *Prunus virginiana*	moist/dry	sun/lt shade	May-June	July-Sept	fair	yes
Flowering* dogwood *Cornus florida*	well-drained/ dry	sun	May-June	Aug-Dec	excellent	yes
Red mulberry *Morus rubra*	moist	sun	May-June	June-July	good	yes
Mountain ash* *Sorbus spp.*	moist/dry	sun/lt shade	May-June	Aug-March	excellent	yes
Crabapple* *Malus spp.*	moist/dry	sun	May	Sept-March	good	no
Hawthorn* *Crataegus spp.*	moist/dry	sun	May-June	Sept-March	excellent	yes
Serviceberry or Juneberry* *Amelanchier spp.*	moist/dry	sun/lt shade	May-June	June-Aug	good	yes
Fire or pin cherry *Prunus pennsylvanica*	moist/dry	sun/lt shade	May-July	July-Oct	fair	yes

common name(s) scientific name	soil moisture (wet to dry)	light tolerance (sun to shade)	flowering dates	fruit/seeds available	ornamental value	native
Tall Shrubs						
Gray dogwood* *Cornus racemosa*	well-drained /dry	sun	June-July	Aug-Oct	good	yes
Tartarian* honeysuckle *Lonicera tatarica*	well-drained/	sun/shade	May-June	June-Aug	fair	no
Highbush blueberry *Vaccinium corymbosum*	wet/dry	sun	May-July	July-Sept	fair	yes
Silky dogwood* *Cornus amomum*	wet/dry	sun/lt shade	May-July	Aug-Oct	fair	yes
Red-osier dogwood* *Cornus stolonifera*	wet/moist	sun	May-June	July-Sept	good	yes
Amur honeysuckle* *Lonicera maacki*	well-drained /dry	sun/shade	May-July	Sept-March	fair	no
Holly* *Ilex spp*	wet/ well-drained	sun/shade	May-June	Aug-June	good/excellent	yes
(in NH, VT, ME, use *Ilex verticillata* or Common Winterberry)						
Elderberry* *Sambucus canadensis*	wet/ well-drained	sun/lt shade	June-July	Aug-Sept	poor	yes
Highbush cranberry *Viburnum trilobum*	wet/ well-drained	sun/lt shade	May-June	Sept-May	good	yes
(Nannyberry or *Viburnum lentago* and other *Viburnum spp.* also possible)						
Northern arrowwood *Viburnum recognitum*	moist/dry	sun/lt shade	May-July	July-Sept	good	yes
Staghorn sumac *Rhus typhina*	well-drained/ dry	sun	June-July	Aug-Sept	good	yes
Medium to low shrubs						
Japanese barberry* *Berberis thunbergii*	moist/dry	sun/lt shade	May	Sept-May	excellent	no
American Blackberry *Rubus allegheniensis*	moist/dry	sun/lt shade	May-July	July-Sept	poor	yes
Raspberry *Rubus spp.*	moist/dry	sun/lt shade	May-June	July-Aug	poor	yes
Blueberry *Vaccinium spp.*	wet/dry	sun/lt shade	May-July	July-Sept	fair	yes
Black Huckleberry *Gaylussacia baccata*	wet/dry	sun/lt shade	May-June	June-Sept	fair	yes

common name(s) scientific name	soil moisture (wet to dry)	light tolerance (sun to shade)	flowering dates	fruit/seeds available	ornamental value	native
Bayberry* *Myrica pennsylvanica*	well-drained	sun/lt shade	May-June	Sept-Jan	fair	yes
Vines						
Virginia creeper* *Parthenocissus quinquefolia*	moist/dry	sun/shade	June-Aug	Sept-Jan	excellent	yes
Bittersweet* *Celastrus scandens*	well-drained/dry	sun/lt shade	May-June	Sept-Dec	excellent	yes
Summer grape *Vitis aestivalis*	moist/dry	sun/lt shade	May-July	Sept-Oct	poor	yes

Indicates which species withstand city conditions.

FLOWERS FOR WILDLIFE

The following list includes recommended flowers to provide important food for butterflies, bees, moths and hummingbirds. Refer to *Landscaping for Wildlife* by Carroll Henderson (see Appendix H) for more detailed listings, or contact your local nursery. Appendix I includes information on seed sources.

Avoid unknown seed mixtures. These may include certain invasive plants, such as purple loosestrife, which are very harmful to the environment.

Wildflowers:

Asters	Black-eyed Susans	Goldenrod
Hawkweed	Milkweed	Phlox

Herbs:

Catnip	Dill	Lemon balm
Marjoram	Parsley	Peppermint

Annuals:

Cosmos	Heliotrope	Impatiens
Marigold	Nasturtium	Phlox, Annual
Sage, Scarlet	Sweet William	Zinnia

Perennials:

Butterfly-weed	Cardinal Flower	Columbine, Wild
Coral bells	Dame's Rocket	Globe Thistle
Lavender	Lupine	Sunflower, Mexican
Sweet William	Violets	

UNIVERSITY OF
NEW HAMPSHIRE
COOPERATIVE EXTENSION

Transplanting Nursery Grown Trees and Shrubs
Charles H. Williams, Extension Specialist, Ornamentals

Many varieties of ornamental and useful trees and shrubs are available throughout the growing season. Your local plant nursery, garden center, and UNH Cooperative Extension office can provide you with additional information on selecting and caring for plants that will be an attractive asset to your property. This leaflet will provide you with some suggestions on proper planting to help insure that your investment gets off to a good start.

Selecting nursery-grown stock has some advantages. Unlike the wild tree, the nursery-grown plant has usually been transplanted and root pruned several times in its early growth. This results in better root development close to the main stem. Nursery-grown plants are usually easier to establish because more roots are also retained in the digging. These plants have been grown for several years with intensive care under local conditions or have been provided by nearby wholesale nursery specialists.

When field-grown trees and shrubs reach a marketable size, they're usually dug during their dormant period and handled in one or more of the following ways:

* They're lifted without a ball of soil around the roots. The bare roots are then surrounded by a moist packing medium and wrapped with a waterproof material to retard drying. These plants are usually offered early in the spring and called, "bare-root stock." Most mail order stock will be bare-root.

* The plants are dug bare root and a synthetic ball, often of some sort of light-weight medium, is molded around their roots. One or more layer of a protective material is then wrapped around the manufactured ball to hold it together and retain moisture. These plants are known as "processed" or "artificial" balls, although they may appear to be similar to regular "B & B" stock.

* The plants are lifted with a ball of soil surrounding the root system. The root balls are then wrapped with burlap or a similar material. They're called, "balled and burlapped" or "B & B" stock.

* The plants are dug and placed in a container for further growth or to be sold directly. These are known as "canned" or "containerized" plants.

Getting Started

It's probably best to have some sort of an idea as to what type of plant you wish to obtain, where you intend using it on your property and what function it will perform. Be sure to select plants hardy enough for your area and suitable in growth characteristics for the site you have in mind. Choose quality plants which are in good condition.

When To Transplant

The optimum time for transplanting is when plants are still dormant in early spring or after they've become dormant in the fall. How long they're dormant depends on the climate as well as the kind of plant. Usually, younger and smaller plants of any species are easier to transplant.

Well-prepared and maintained "B & B" or container-grown plants will have the least transplanting physiological shock so they can essentially be planted any time. "Bare-root" plants have the shortest "shelf-life" and should be planted early and as soon as possible.

Transplant when the ground isn't frozen and is workable without the danger of compaction.

Spring planting is advisable for some species and in areas which have severe winters. Transplant in the spring if you live in an area with strong, drying winds, deficient soil moisture, or deeply-frozen ground during the winter months. This applies to evergreens as well as to deciduous plants.

In general, evergreens as a group are usually planted earlier in the fall and later in the spring than deciduous plants. In the fall, plant when their new growth has hardened (September), until about a month before the surface of the ground freezes at night.

Pruning

With purchased professionally prepared nursery stock there should be no need for any pruning to balance top growth and a reduced root system. At the time of planting pruning is usually restricted to the removal of any damaged or broken roots and branches.

The University of New Hampshire Cooperative Extension is an equal opportunity educator and employer. UNH, U.S. Department of Agriculture and the N.H. counties cooperating.

Site and Soil Considerations

After selecting your tree or shrub, the planting site should be evaluated and prepared. Before doing any digging be sure you know the location of any underground utilities or pipes.

Most tree and shrub species have either evolved or have been selected to grow under a range of conditions. Many may have a optimum growth environment but will tolerate a variety of situations.

A good soil will provide adequate drainage, moisture and nutrient retention, aeration, and the proper degree of soil acidity.

The texture and composition of the soil affects drainage and aeration. If drainage is poor, water will collect around the roots and cause them to rot. If aeration is poor, oxygen can't reach the roots through the soil and the plant will suffocate. This is particularly true when transplanting into heavy clay soil.

If soil is too light and lacks organic matter, it won't hold soil nutrients and an adequate amount of water around the roots. This is a problem with very sandy soils. Keep in mind most root activity will be in the top two feet of soil.

Usually the existing soil at the site will be adequate. However, if you are faced with only rubble fill, shallow soil over a hard pan or rock ledge, or only poor subsoil at a highly disturbed construction site, you may want to consider installing a drainage system and bringing in a sufficient quantity of good topsoil to plant into by:

1. Constructing a raised bed with better soil

2. Creating a large planting pocket

Another option would be to amend extremely poor soil with peat, compost, or other good topsoil. However, keep in mind the plant may eventually have to grow and function in your native soil. In extreme cases, if you do too good a job of enhancing the backfill only, roots may remain confined to the original planting hole. See additional comments under the sections on bare root and B & B planting.

Fertilization At Planting

Trees and shrubs are not likely to starve to death the first year, however, many have been damaged or killed by misguided intentions and copious amounts of fresh manure or chemical fertilizers. Consequently, usually little or no fertilization is often suggested at the time of planting. The best answer though would be to have a soil test run to determine if there are any serious deficiencies or nutrient imbalances noted. If, for example, phosphorous is lacking and the pH of the soil needs to be adjusted to between 5.5 and 6.5, it might be advisable to rectify the situation now since both these factors are relatively slow to correct from surface applications.

Digging A Better Hole

The next step in the planting procedure is to dig a hole of ample size. If space is restricted, as in some urban sites, try to dig a hole at least one foot larger than the diameter of the ball or container in which the plant is growing. In more normal situations, try to dig a hole that is at least twice as wide as the existing root system for a sandy soil location. In a heavy clay soil site strive to have a hole that is at least three times the diameter of the root ball.

The hole should be deep enough to allow the tree or shrub to be placed about as deep as it grew in the nursery.

If the hole is dug with a power auger, the soil on the sides and bottom of the hole should be loosened with a shovel since the action of an auger often causes these areas to become compacted. Roots will not readily penetrate a compacted soil and may be confined to the small area of the hole.

Planting Bare-Root Nursery Stock

Plant as soon as possible after the plants are obtained. Remove the decorative and protective outer wrappings and inspect the root system upon arrival. If the roots appear dry, water them or immerse them in a container of water overnight. Do not keep most plants in water longer than 24 hours.

If planting must be deferred for a number of days, store the re-wrapped plants in a cool location. Be sure the roots are not exposed to freezing temperatures and are kept moist. Another alternative would be to heel them in a shallow trench outdoors in a shaded protected location until planting time.

Always keep the roots covered with soil, wet burlap, or packing material, or in a container of water while being moved to the planting site.

All broken and mangled roots should be cut back to sound tissue with a sharp knife, and jagged ends of the larger roots should be trimmed smooth.

Dig the planting hole as large as feasible. Prepare a hole that is two or three times the spread of the root system or at least loosen the soil for that distance from the center of the hole. Dig the hole deep enough to accommodate the plant at the same level as it originally grew, as determined by the soil-stained ring at the base of the trunk. It's a well-known fact that trees set too deeply won't thrive, and may even die within a few years.

Trees with graft or bud unions should be planted so the union or swelling near the crown is below the soil surface to encourage rooting from the variety stem. With dwarf apple trees and similar plants grafted onto rootstocks or intermediate stocks which are designed to control size, the grafting union should always be clearly visible above the soil.

If the soil is heavy and compacted, loosen the soil at the bottom and sides of the hole to encourage root penetration and better drainage. Because the roots usually grow downward at a slight angle from the horizontal, it's wise to make a cone-shaped mound of soil at the bottom. The root crown can then be set on this mound and the roots spread over and down the sides. Work two or three shovelsful of soil under and around the roots to eliminate air pockets which could dry them out. You might want to plant slightly higher to allow for two to three inches of ultimate settling.

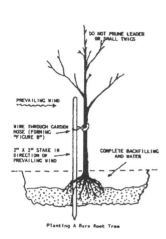

Planting A Bare Root Tree

Unless the soil at the site is totally unacceptable, bare-root material should be planted into the same soil that came out of the hole. The bare roots will acclimate to their new surroundings and growth will occur accordingly.

Next, continue to add backfill soil until the hole is about 2/3 full after being tamped. Then add gallons of water to settle the soil further and to eliminate air pockets.

When the water has drained down, the remainder of the hole is filled with soil, leaving a saucer-like depression to make subsequent watering of the tree easier. A ridge of soil or sod 4-6" high placed in a circle 2-3 feet away from the trunk to form a basin is an aid in holding water from rainfall and irrigation.

In exposed sites most bare-root trees benefit from some sort of extra support for the first two years after transplanting. It is desirable to hold the plant firmly to prevent shifting or root damage during windy rainstorms, however, allow the upper portion of the tree some flexibility.

Larger trees can be secured by several stakes or guywires. A small tree can be secured to a stake by threading a rope or wire through a short length of garden hose to prevent injury to the bark. Twist the wire around the trunk and stake in the form of a "figure 8" and fasten to the stake (see drawing). Other methods can also be used such as broad, strap-like ties to secure the tree.

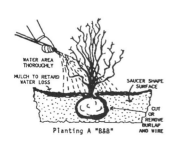

Planting A "B&B"

Most shrubs will probably not require any staking unless planted in extreme exposed, windy locations.

Planting Balled and Burlapped Plants

Broadleaf and narrowleaf evergreens, large trees, and deciduous woody plants which are difficult to ship or transplant are sold with a root-soil ball wrapped in burlap. Some may have an additional plastic wrapping.

Be sure to carry the plant by the soil ball only, since rough handling of the plant may cause the ball to break or roots to pull loose from the soil ball. Avoid dropping the plants. Prior to planting keep the plants in a cool protected location and well watered.

The planting hole should be about twice to three times the width of the root ball and be well-drained, especially for yews and most broadleaf evergreens. The hole should be deep enough so the plant will be about at the same level it grew in the nursery.

Often the B & B tree or shrub can be planted in the same soil that came out of the hole. However, because the nursery plant has evolved and is presently growing in a certain type of soil, problems could arise if that soil type is dramatically different from soil at the site. Consequently, there may be some benefit to creating a transition zone of amended soil as the backfill material. This would be a mixture of the existing soil from the hole, other topsoil, and up to 25 percent peat moss, compost, etc.

If need be in heavy compacted soil, loosen the soil at the bottom and sides of the hole to again help drainage and ultimate root penetration.

The plant should be centered and placed at the bottom of the hole making sure there is firm contact between the bottom of the plant and the soil in the hole. When air is trapped under the ball, trouble may develop later. If required set the plant on a cushion of a modified soil mix so the top of the ball is about level with or slightly above the surrounding ground.

Larger specimens may come wrapped in burlap with the ball supported by a wire basket. Often the wire mesh may be large enough to allow future root penetration without girdling. However, if it can be done carefully without breaking the ball, the wire can be cut, folded down, or removed entirely. The same goes for the burlap. Regular burlap and natural rope materials soon rot away in the soil; however, plastics, synthetic or treated burlap and twine may persist and cause problems for the plant later on.

Backfill around the ball until the hole is about 1/2 filled. Then tamp gently and completely soak the soil in the hole. This will help drive out any trapped air. The backfilling may now be completed. Using the soil which is left over, form a saucer-shaped depression.

Fill it with water and let it drain completely. If the soil settles, add more soil and water again.

Planting Container-Grown Plants

Two general types of containers are used by nurseries: 1) those that are reusable or at least won't readily decompose (metal cans, special fabric, plastic, wood, or clay); 2) those which will decompose (paper, peat, or wood fiber).

Usually it is best to remove the plant from the container, even the so-called biodegradable ones. On smaller thin-walled peat pots used for seedlings or transplants you can roll down or remove 1/3 of the top of the material on a decomposable container. If any part of this type of container is exposed to the surface air, it may act as a wick and tend to dry out the entire root ball. Heavy cloth-like growing bags must be carefully cut away from the root ball. If roots circle the soil ball next to the container wall, the

plant is said to be pot-bound. Spread out or cut the larger roots in three or four places to reduce the possibility of girdling roots later.

Again dig a hole at least two to three times the diameter of the container. The depth should be about the height of the container itself.

For container production nursery operators use a variety of growing media. It may be an amended soil mix or one made up of peat, sand, composted bark, or other inorganic or organic components. Consequently, while many native soils may be compatible and could be used directly from the hole as backfill, the preparation of a transition zone may help the container plant off to a better start. The same blend suggested for B & B stock could be utilized or if the soil is sandy, a good fibrous peat or compost may be added to the same volume of soil. For a soil that's very heavy and wet, add an equal volume of sand or perlite, and coarse organic matter.

Next, proceed to backfill around the root ball. Firm the soil and water the plant well. Taller trees and shrubs in extreme exposed sites may also be either staked or supported by guy wires until the plant is well established in two years.

Most nurseries have a regular fertilization program or use a slow-release material in their containers, fertilizer is usually not needed the first year.

Post-Planting Care

Watering. It's easy to understand why your plants need water the first day to settle the soil around the roots; but regular watering all during the following growing season is also needed. Supplement natural rainfall, as necessary, to supply one inch each week.

Trees will require 15-30 gallons and shrubs 5-10 gallons every week when die from lack of water even when homeowners think they're giving them enough. Avoid keeping the plants too wet, though, because roots also need oxygen to function properly.

In winter, evergreens retain their leaves and continue to lose water through them. For this reason, evergreens should be watered during the late fall. Deciduous plants don't need watering in the winter since they're dormant and won't lose much moisture.

Pruning. Remove any damaged branches and those that don't conform to desired shape. Twigs and buds along the branches and upper parts of the trunk shouldn't be removed until the tree is well established. Don't cut back the leader of a tree, such as a pin oak which grows with a single trunk. Prune most trees in the spring before growth begins. In many cases, the nursery may have already done most of the pruning for you. However, check for crossing or rubbing branches and eliminate any multiple leaders and weak, sharp-angled branch crotches early in the tree's development.

Check the plants. At least once a month, check the plants for any cultural or environmental stress. Also look for evidence of any insect or disaease problems. At this point, too, make sure all strings, tags, or wires around the plant have been removed since they also can cause gridling and, in time, kill the plant.

Cultivation. Shallow cultivation one inch deep around a new unmulched planting controls weeds or lawn grasses that compete with your plant's roots.

Mulching. After planting, you can mulch the soil beneath the branches with a two- to four-inch layer of coarse organic material or leafy compost. Other materials can also be used to conserve moisture and curtail weed growth such as the fabric weed barriers.

Fertilizing. If you use plenty of rich topsoil for backfilling, newly transplanted trees and shrubs aren't likely to need fertilizer for the first year. However, if immediate growth seems stunted or leaves are paled, fertilizing is advisable after the first year. Apply fertilizer in the fall or early spring--not in midsummer. If no soil test was run, use a complete general fertilizer following label instructions. New, small, young bare-root plants may benefit from a liquid "starter fertilization" during a cold, wet spring.

Other items. To reduce damage by rabbits or mice, use wire or plastic guards and keep the mulch away from the trunk or stem of the plants. Mow nearby vegetation in the fall. Avoid bark injury from lawnmowers and string trimmers. Do not apply lawn weed killers near woody ornamental plants.

Appendix F
Construction Specifications for Nest Boxes

We've selected three common New England species that utilize nest boxes — Big Brown Bat, Wood Duck, and Eastern Bluebird — which you can expect to find on or near your schoolyard site. The discussion and construction notes below will assist you in building these boxes, using the plans that follow. These plans can be adapted for other cavity-nesting wildlife species as well. Refer to the accompanying chart for correct dimensions, and to Carrol Henderson's *Woodworking for Wildlife* (listed in Appendix H) for more nest box specifications and plans.

NEST SPECIFICATIONS

Species	Floor of Cavity Inches	Depth of Cavity Inches	Entrance Above Floor Inches	Diameter of Entrance Inches	Height Above Ground Feet
Bluebird	5x5	8	6	1-1/2	5-10
Robin	6x8	8			6-15
Chickadee	4x4	8-10	6-8	1-1/8	6-15
Titmouse	4x4	8-10	6-8	1-1/4	6-15
Nuthatch	4x4	8-10	6-8	1-1/4	12-20
House Wren	4x4	6-8	1-6	1 to 1-1/4	6-10
Tree Swallow	5x5	6	1-5	1-1/2	10-15
Barn Swallow	6x6	6			8-12
Purple Martin	6x6	6	1	2-1/2	15-20
Phoebe	6x6	6			8-12
Flicker	7x7	16-18	14-16	2-1/2	6-20
Downy Woodpecker	4x4	9-12	6-8	1-1/4	6-20
Hairywoodpecker	6x6	12-15	9-12	1-1/2	12-20
Screech owl	8x8	12-15	9-12	3	10-30
Saw-whet owl	6x6	10-12	8-10	2-1/2	12-20
Wood duck	10-18	12-24	12-16	4	10-20

BATS

Organic Insect Control

The most likely occupants of bat houses in New England are the big brown bat and the little brown bat. Who in the world would think of building a house for bats? The idea sounds farfetched. Once bats are understood, however, their desirable qualities exceed even those of the popular purple martin.

For example, some people claim that purple martins eat up to a thousand mosquitoes per day. Other persons dispute that total, saying that the daily total is much lower because martins don't actively feed when mosquitoes are most active. In contrast, bats do. A single, big brown bat can eat 3,000 to 7,000 mosqitoes each night! And a big brown bat can live up to 19 years.

Bats are also devoted parents. Expectant mother bats join together in "nursery" colonies where they congregate to raise their young. Mother bats help each other with rearing young, and each female recognizes her own. The big brown bat raises just one young per year.

Since bats are such an important form of natural control for insect "pests" like mosquitoes, it is in our own best interest to perpetuate them. This is already being done in much of Europe where bats are totally protected and where people build "bat houses" much like we build martin houses.

Notes on Construction

The most critical dimension is the three-fourth-inch width of the entry space. All inner surfaces must be roughened with a chisel or saw cuts to permit bats to climb on them with ease. Rough outer surfaces are also preferred.

Temperature

Daytime temperatures in the bat house must be very hot — about 80-90 degrees Fahrenheit. One way to achieve this is to cover the bat house on top and a couple inches down the sides with two or more layers of tar paper. The dark color of the paper absorbs heat from the sun; the paper also helps protect the bats from the rain. Since tar paper may be hard to attach and may weather badly, another alternative is to paint the bat house black so it will absorb heat from the sunlight.

Larger houses provide greater temperature stability, as do tight fitting tops and sides. Attaching the bat house to a building may further increase temperature stability. Taller roosts provide temperature gradients, permitting bats to move vertically in seeking their preference.

Placement of Bat Boxes

Bat houses should be oriented to receive maximum solar radiation, especially in the morning. Preferred sites are also those protected from wind. Ideally, in New England a bat house should be mounted on the southeast side of a building or tree, roughly 12 to 15 feet above the ground.

The best habitat for bat house placement is near a permanent source of water where insects abound. The closer a bat house is to a marsh, lake, river or farm pond, the greater the probability of it being used. In addition to the presence of nearby water, the habitat chosen for box placement should be at least 40 percent nonforested within a 180 acre area.

Bat houses should be placed by early April. It bats do not find or use the house within two years, move it to another location. In some areas heavy use of pesticides, a lack of hibernating sites, too great a distance to feeding or drinking sites, or even an abundance of already available summer roosting sites may preclude occupation. Once occupied, bat houses should not be disturbed and need not be cleaned.

It may be possible or desirable to set up an alternative bat house so they don't take up residence in someone else's house. Sometimes bats create severe problems for people by establishing huge colonies in the attics of homes. The best way to solve this problem is to hire a carpenter in the winter to exclude bats at the holes where they enter the house. Since most bats migrate, it is possible to exclude bats while they are not present.

Bats and Rabies

What about rabies? In 40 years of record keeping in the United States, only 10 people are believed to have contracted rabies from bats. In contrast, more people die in one year from bee stings, dog attacks, or even from food poisoning contracted at church picnics. If we simply leave bats alone, the odds of being harmed by one are minuscule. They don't even remotely compare to the generally accepted dangers of having pets or driving to work! With or without bats nearby, the most important action you can take to protect your family from rabies is to vaccinate your family dogs and cats.

This information on bats and bat houses was provided by Dr. Merlin D. Tuttle, Bat Conservation International, PO Box 162603, Austin, Texas 78716. More detailed information on these subjects can be obtained from this same address.

WOOD DUCK

The traditional wood duck box has helped the beautiful wood duck make a remarkable recovery during the past 20 years. Early in this century some people believed the wood duck was becoming extinct. Now it is an abundant waterfowl species.

Notes on Construction

As shown in the plans, the entrance hole should be an oval, 3 inches high and 4 inches wide. This hole excludes most raccoons. The hole should be centered 19 inches above the floor. An 18 inch x 3 inch strip of 1/4 inch mesh hardware cloth attached inside the box under the entrance will function as a ladder for the newly hatched ducklings. Sometimes squirrels will tear this ladder loose, so it will need to be checked annually. Alternatively, the wood under the entrance hole can be roughened with a chisel to give the ducklings the toeholds they need. The roughened area should extend below the entrance hole for 1 foot.

Place at least 3 inches of chain saw wood chips in the box to serve as nesting material. Paired roofing nails with large heads should be used around the top of the box to wire it shut so raccoons can't open it.

Construct the house of wood that is strong and can be made weather resistant. It may be painted, stained or treated; however, such treatment is not necessary if weather resistant lumber is used — on the outside only. The floor should be recessed 1/4 inch up from the lower edge of the sides to prevent rotting.

Placement of Wood Duck Boxes

Houses can be erected on an isolated tree or on a 16-foot long, 4 inch x 4 inch post of cypress, cedar or preservative-treated wood. An aluminum or tin sheet should be nailed around the post under the house to prevent squirrels and raccoons from entering. Used aluminum printing plates from newspaper offices can be purchased very cheaply and stapled lengthwise to the 4 inch x 4 inch post under the nest box. Since wood ducks are not territorial, two or more houses can be placed on the same post.

Vigilant starling control will be necessary in wood duck boxes. Repeated evidence of starling nesting material (up to six times) will generally discourage further attempts. The top of a wood duck box should be fastened to its support so that it leans forward a couple of inches; this facilitates the drainage of rainwater. To strengthen the box, nail a 9-3/4 inch long 1 inch x2 inch along the inside top edge of the front. Nail a similar size piece onto the back just under where the roof rests.

Boxes placed on posts in water should be about 5 feet above the water's surface. Boxes placed upland on trees should be at least 8 feet, and preferably above 20 feet high. Boxes can be placed over water or in woodland habitat up to half-a-mile from lakes, ponds, marshes and rivers.

Box entrances near water should face the water. Otherwise, there seems to be a slight preference for south- and west-facing entrance holes. Ideally, boxes on land should be 30 to 100 feet from the water's edge. The chance of predation by raccoons is higher along the water's edge.

Complete annual maintenance on wood duck boxes by March 1.

EASTERN BLUEBIRD

Eastern bluebirds are one of the most popular songbirds in New England. Their brilliant blue colors, delightful calls, clean habits and family devotion have long provided happiness and inspiration to people.

Habitat for a Bluebird

Ideal bluebird habitat is comprised of mixed hardwood forests and grasslands. The grassy areas may be either meadows, old fields, pastures, yards, cemeteries, or highway rights-of-way. It is best if the grass is short or sparse. Mowed or grazed areas provide good habitat. There shoud be either power lines, fence posts or scattered trees in grassy areas to provide feeding perches. Bluebirds will sometimes nest in the backyards of homes in rural areas or on the fringe of urban areas. They normally nest in rural areas, but away from farmstead buildings where competition from house sparrows is usually more severe.

Bluebird nests are neat, cup-shaped structures made of fine grass. There are usually five pale blue eggs in a clutch.

Construction of Two Nest Box Types

The Peterson bluebird house is the best type. It is relatively safe for blue-birds and is easily checked and cleaned. The seven parts of this house are assembled in this order: First, the inner roof is toe-nailed to the top of the back. Second, the floor is toe-nailed to the back, 10-1/2 inches below the top. Third, one side is nailed to the resulting frame, then the other side is nailed to the frame. Next the swing-down front is fastened by nailing one nail to each side of the base. A third nail is pounded part way into the side, the same level as the entrance hole. This is pulled out each time the house is checked. Finally, the outer roof is nailed on top. The top primarily serves as a cat guard.

A one-board bluebird house is much easier to build than the Peterson house, and is included here for the benefit of young people or for adults who do not have access to table saws or radial arm saws. This type of house is more vulnerable to predation by house cats, so it's best used on free-standing posts which have tin or aluminum sheets stapled around the support post. Some people feel that sparrow use in the one-board house can be discouraged by cutting a 3-inch diameter hole in the roof and covering the hole with 1/4- or 1/2-inch hardware cloth. Bluebirds don't seem to mind the "sunroof," but sparrows may be discouraged by it.

If an oblong hole is not used, either drill a 1-1/2 inch hole (a larger hole is accessible to starlings), or try a slot entrance. When given a choice, bluebirds build more nests in boxes with a front slot entrance, than in boxes with circular entrances. If starlings are a problem, use a 1-3/16 inch slot; if not, use a 1-3/8 inch slot.

Placement of Bluebird Boxes

Both the Peterson and one-board bluebird houses should be placed 4 to 6 feet above the ground and spaced about 100 yards apart. The entrance hole should face north, east or northeast to prevent sunlight from shining into the hole and overheating the box interior.

A bluebird trail consists of five or more houses placed along a road or fenceline. The houses should be ready by late March and can be checked every 7 to 10 days from late March until mid August. Remove a nest as soon as a brood leaves its nest box. This allows a second brood to be raised.

Parasite Prevention

To prevent blowfly parasites on young bluebirds (and other species) bend a piece of 3/8 inch mesh hardware cloth, so that it sits 1 inch off the bot-tom of the box and covers the entire floor. The blowfly larvae will fall through the wire and be unable to get back up to the nest. (This "trap" was designed by Ira Campbell of Timberville, Virginia.)

Materials for this appendix excerpted or adapted with permission from:

Henderson, Carrol. 1987. *Woodworking for Wildlife.* Minnesota Department of Natural Resources, St. Paul

PLAN 10
BAT HOUSE
(SMALL)

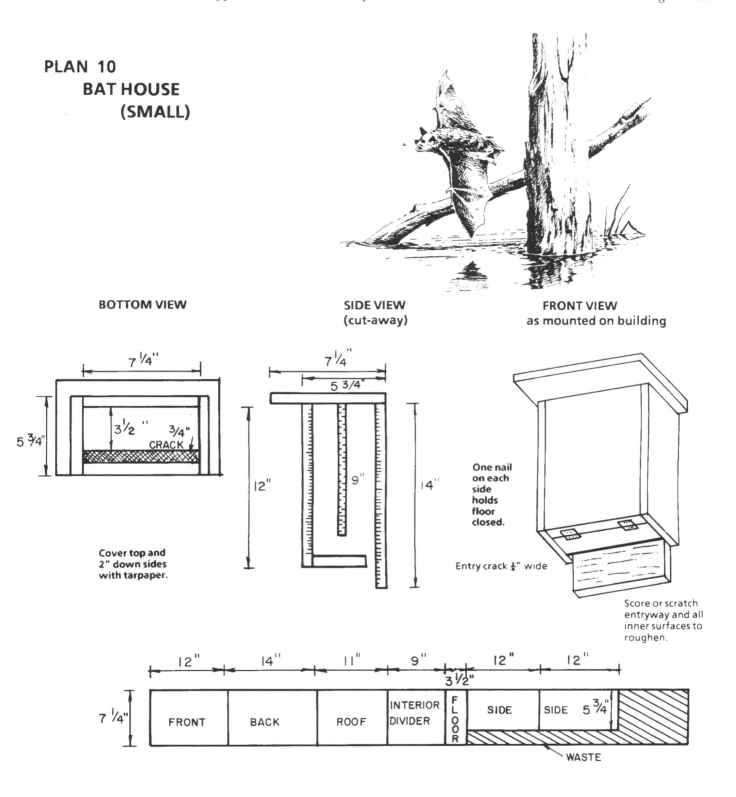

BOTTOM VIEW

7 ¼"

5 ¾"

3½"   ¾"
CRACK

Cover top and
2" down sides
with tarpaper.

SIDE VIEW
(cut-away)

7 ¼"
5 ¾"

12"   9"   14"

FRONT VIEW
as mounted on building

One nail
on each
side
holds
floor
closed.

Entry crack ¼" wide

Score or scratch
entryway and all
inner surfaces to
roughen.

12"   14"   11"   9"   12"   12"
3½"

7 ¼"

| FRONT | BACK | ROOF | INTERIOR DIVIDER | FLOOR | SIDE | SIDE 5 ¾" | |

WASTE

LUMBER: One 1" X 8" X 8'0"

PLAN 15
NEST BOX FOR:
COMMON & HOODED MERGANSER
WOOD DUCK
RACCOON
FOX and GRAY SQUIRREL
PILEATED WOODPECKER

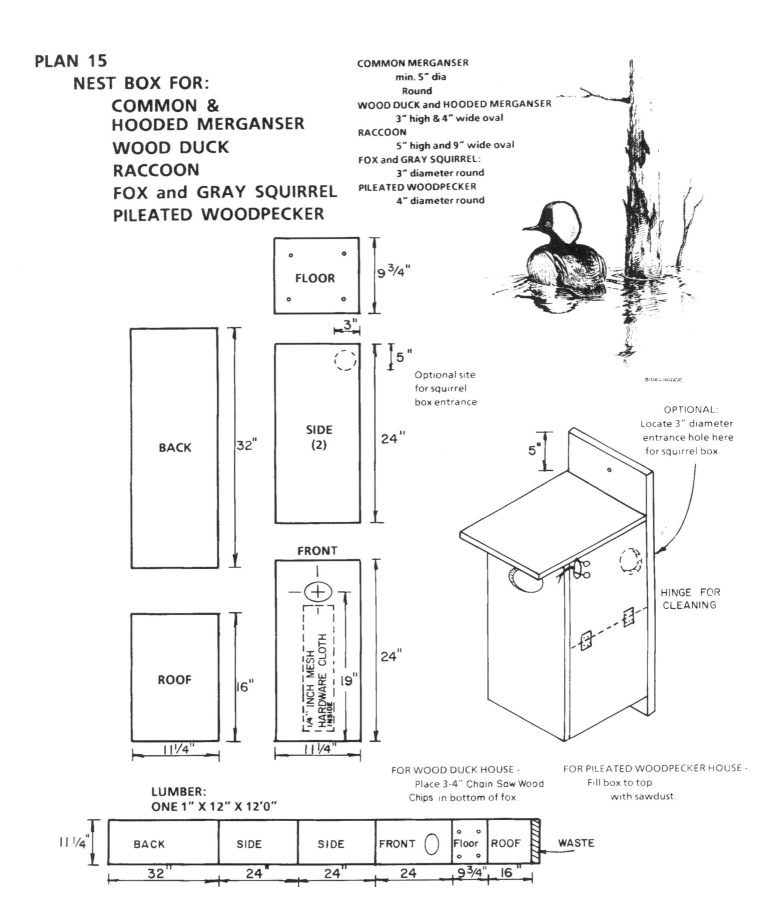

COMMON MERGANSER
   min. 5" dia
   Round
WOOD DUCK and HOODED MERGANSER
   3" high & 4" wide oval
RACCOON
   5" high and 9" wide oval
FOX and GRAY SQUIRREL:
   3" diameter round
PILEATED WOODPECKER
   4" diameter round

SIDELINGER.

FLOOR   9 3/4"

3"

SIDE (2)   5"

Optional site
for squirrel
box entrance

24"

BACK   32"

OPTIONAL:
Locate 3" diameter
entrance hole here
for squirrel box

5"

HINGE FOR
CLEANING

FRONT

1/4" INCH MESH
HARDWARE CLOTH
INSIDE

19"   24"

ROOF   16"

11 1/4"   11 1/4"

FOR WOOD DUCK HOUSE -
Place 3-4" Chain Saw Wood
Chips in bottom of fox.

FOR PILEATED WOODPECKER HOUSE -
Fill box to top
with sawdust.

LUMBER:
ONE 1" X 12" X 12'0"

11 1/4"	BACK	SIDE	SIDE	FRONT ⬭	Floor	ROOF	WASTE
	32"	24"	24"	24	9 3/4"	16"	

PLAN 5
NEST BOX FOR:
TREE SWALLOW
EASTERN BLUEBIRD
GREAT CRESTED FLYCATCHER

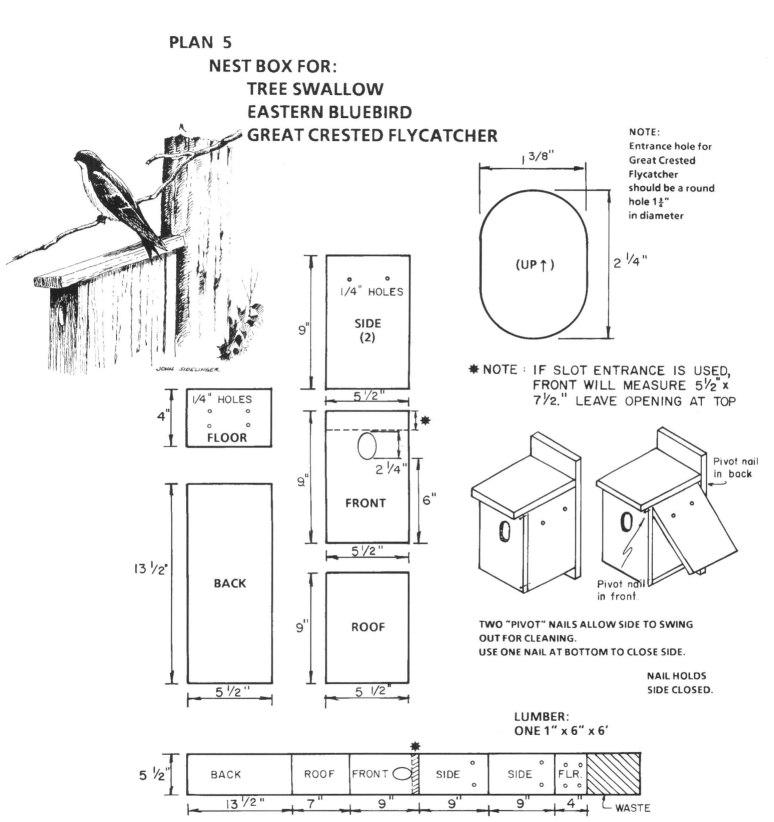

NOTE:
Entrance hole for
Great Crested
Flycatcher
should be a round
hole 1¾"
in diameter

1 3/8"

(UP ↑)   2 1/4"

✳ NOTE : IF SLOT ENTRANCE IS USED,
FRONT WILL MEASURE 5½" x
7½." LEAVE OPENING AT TOP

1/4" HOLES

SIDE
(2)

9"

5 1/2"

1/4" HOLES

FLOOR

4"

FRONT

9"   6"

2 1/4"

5 1/2"

BACK

13 1/2"

5 1/2"

ROOF

9"

5 1/2"

JOHN SIDELINGER

Pivot nail
in back

Pivot nail
in front.

TWO "PIVOT" NAILS ALLOW SIDE TO SWING
OUT FOR CLEANING.
USE ONE NAIL AT BOTTOM TO CLOSE SIDE.

NAIL HOLDS
SIDE CLOSED.

LUMBER:
ONE 1" x 6" x 6'

5 1/2"

| BACK | ROOF | FRONT | SIDE | SIDE | FLR. | WASTE |

13 1/2"   7"   9"   9"   9"   4"

PLAN 4
PETERSON BLUEBIRD HOUSE

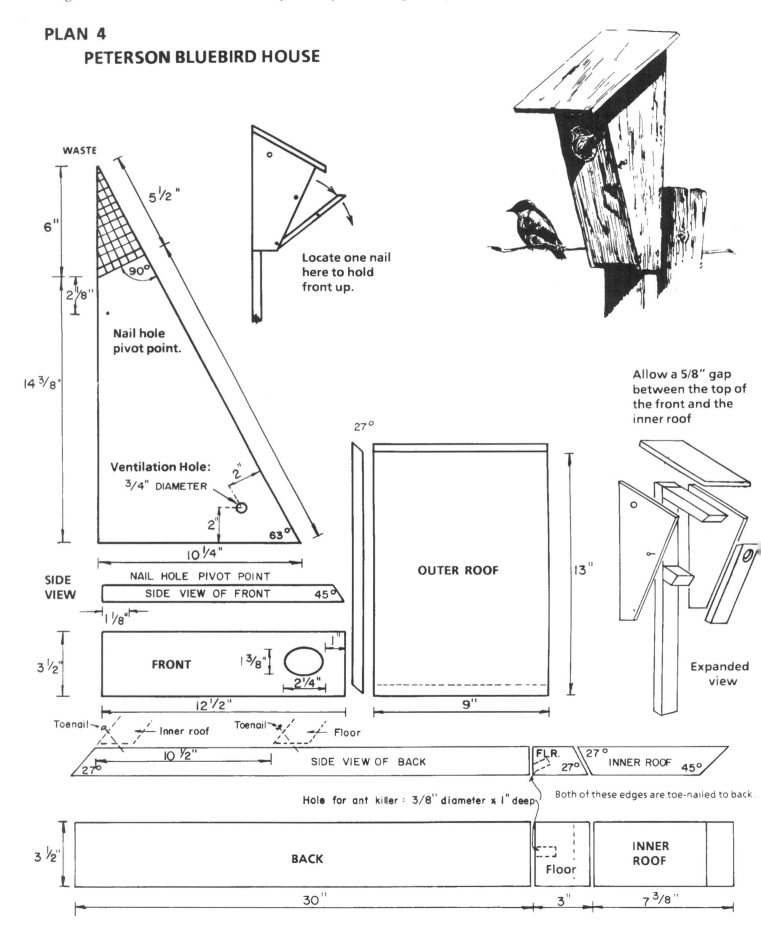

WASTE

6"

5½"

90°

2⅛"

Nail hole pivot point.

Locate one nail here to hold front up.

14⅜"

Ventilation Hole:
¾" DIAMETER

2"

2"

63°

10¼"

Allow a 5/8" gap between the top of the front and the inner roof

27°

OUTER ROOF

13"

9"

Expanded view

SIDE VIEW

NAIL HOLE PIVOT POINT
SIDE VIEW OF FRONT   45°

1⅛"

FRONT

3½"

1⁣3/8"   1"

2¼"

12½"

Toenail — Inner roof   Toenail — Floor

10½"   SIDE VIEW OF BACK   FLR.   27°   INNER ROOF   45°

27°   27°

Hole for ant killer: 3/8" diameter x 1" deep   Both of these edges are toe-nailed to back.

3½"   BACK   INNER ROOF

Floor

30"   3"   7⅜"

PLAN 25   ENTRANCE HOLE SIZES FOR DUCK, MERGANSER, AND RACCOON NEST BOXES.

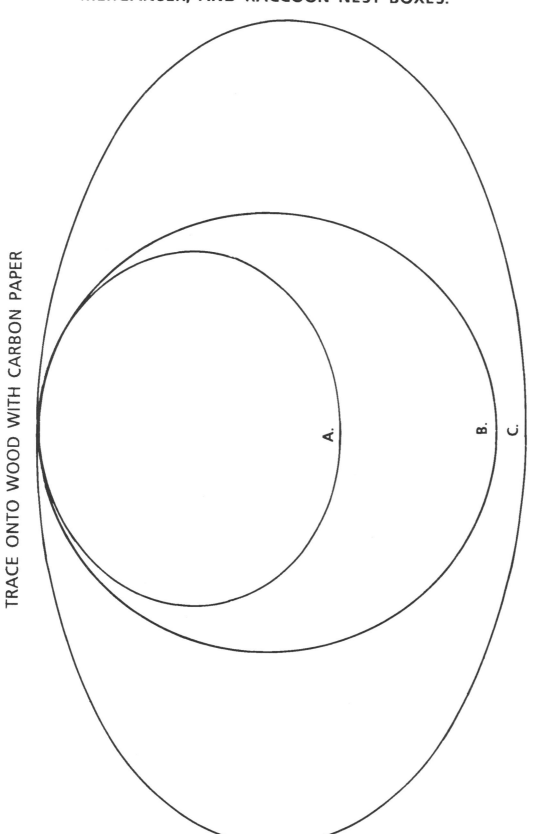

TRACE ONTO WOOD WITH CARBON PAPER

A.

B.

C.

A. WOOD DUCK AND HOODED MERGANSER

B. COMMON MERGANSER

C. RACCOON

PLAN 24   ENTRANCE HOLE SIZES FOR SONGBIRD, WOODPECKER, AND SQUIRREL NEST BOXES.

TRACE ONTO WOOD WITH CARBON PAPER

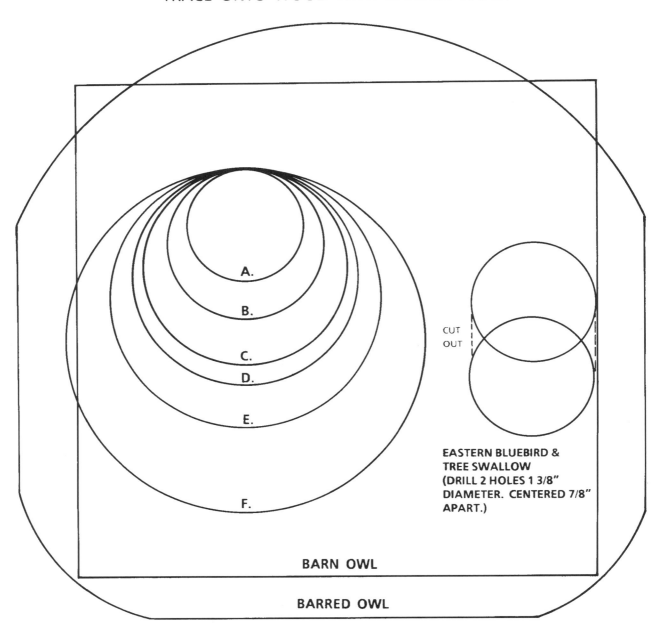

A.
B.
C.
D.
E.
F.

CUT OUT

EASTERN BLUEBIRD & TREE SWALLOW (DRILL 2 HOLES 1 3/8" DIAMETER. CENTERED 7/8" APART.)

BARN OWL

BARRED OWL

A.   HOUSE WREN, BLACK-CAPPED CHICKADEE, WHITE-BREASTED NUTHATCH, TUFTED TITMOUSE AND PROTHONOTARY WARBLER
B.   GREAT CRESTED FLYCATCHER
C.   PURPLE MARTIN
D.   COMMON FLICKER
E.   GRAY AND FOX SQUIRREL, SCREECH OWL, AND AMERICAN KESTRAL
F.   PILEATED WOODPECKER

Appendix G
Resource Agencies

NATIONAL RESOURCES

Wildlife Organizations

Urban Wildlife Resources
5130 W. Running Brook Rd.
Columbia, MD 21044
Tel: 410-997-7161
Fax: 410-997-6849
Quarterly newsletter; write for publications list.

National Institute for Urban Wildlife
P.O. Box 3015
Shepherdstown, WV 25443

National Wildlife Federation
1412 Sixteenth St., N.W.
Washington, D.C. 20036
National Wildlife magazine; *Ranger Rick*, a magazine for children;
    "Gardening with Wildlife" kit.

Wildlife Management Institute
709 Wire Building
1000 Vermont Avenue, N.W.
Washington, D.C. 20005
Brochures such as "Helping Wildlife: Working with Nature";
    write for publications list.

National Wildflower Research Center
4801 La Crosse Avenue
Austin, Texas 78739
This nonprofit wildflower research center, established in 1983 by Mrs.
Lyndon B. Johnson and associates, investigates and promotes research
on wildflowers and disseminates information about their use in the
landscape. Enclose SASE with your inquiry.

Bat Conservation International
PO Box 162603
Austin, TX 78716

Lepidopterists' Society
Natural History Museum of Los Angeles County
900 Exposition Blvd.
Los Angeles, CA 90007

Bird Societies

National Audubon Society
Educational Services
950 Third Avenue
New York, NY 10022
Publishes the monthly Audubon magazine; has 450 local chapters.

Bird Feeders Society
PO Box 225
Mystic, CT 06355
Publishes the quarterly magazine *Around the Bird Feeder*.

North American Bluebird Society
Box 6295
Silver Spring, MD 20906
Publishes the quarterly journal *Salia*.

Native Plant Organizations

Center for Plant Conservation
P.O. Box 299
St. Louis, MO 63166

The Nature Conservancy
1815 North Lynn St.
Arlington, VA 22209
For information on regional chapters, call 703-247-3724

Society for
Ecological Restoration
Madison Arboretum
University of Wisconsin
1207 Seminole Highway
Madison, WI 53711

REGIONAL ORGANIZATIONS — NEW ENGLAND

New England Wild Flower Society, Inc.
Garden in the Woods
180 Hemenway Rd.
Framingham, MA 01701-2699
Tel: 508-877-7630

STATE RESOURCES – NEW HAMPSHIRE

New Hampshire has a great many organizations and agencies that provide information and education, much of it free of charge. The list below is not intended to be complete, but provides a basic reference guide.

Federal Agencies
US Department of Agriculture

Forest Service
PO Box 640
Durham, NH 03824
868-5576

Durham is the site of a field office of the State and Private Forestry branch of the Forest Service, which provides cooperative forestry assistance. The staff of the Durham office includes specialists in forest management, and forest insects and diseases, who will answer general forestry questions and provide free literature for the public.

USDA Soil Conservation Service

Federal Building
Durham, NH 03824
868-7581

The Soil Conservation Service (SCS) provides assistance to landowners primarily through locally organized conservation districts. You can get basic information about the soils in your area through SCS.

Natural Resources Conservation Service and District Offices

Belknap County	Carroll County
Laconia, 528-8713	Conway, 447-2771
Cheshire County	Coos County
Keene, 352-3602	Lancaster, 788-4651
Grafton County	Hillsborough County
Woodsville, 747-2001	Milford, 673-2409
Merrimack County	Rockingham County
Concord, 225-6401	Exeter, 772-4385
Strafford County	Sullivan County
Dover, 749-3037	Claremont, 542-6681

State Agencies

NH Divison of Forests and Lands
105 Loudon Road
Concord, NH 03301
271-2214 or 271-3456

The NH Division of Forests and Lands was established in 1910 as the State Forestry Department with the general aim of protection and improvement of the state's forests. The Division offers public programs on insect and disease protection, provides nursery stock, and offers advice and assistance in assessing and planning forest resources.

NH Department of Fish & Game
2 Hazen Drive
Concord, NH 03301
271-3421

The NH Fish and Game Department provides technical assistance on a limited basis, for landowners who are interested in habitat management and management and protection of wetlands.

Fish and Game Regional Offices
Region 1 - Lancaster, 788-3164
Region 2 - New Hampton, 744-5470
Region 3 - Durham, 868-1095
Region 4 - Keene, 352-9669

Geological Information Survey (GIS)
University of New Hampshire
862-1792

This system provides a computer survey of state topographical and geological information, including surface waters, town boundaries, soils, bedrock, and groundwater. Mapping is not yet complete for all areas of the state. A statewide data network is being developed. Digital data and hard copy maps are available for a fee. Call for information.

State-County Agencies

University of New Hampshire Cooperative Extension
State Office
Natural Resources
Pettee Hall - UNH
Durham, NH 03824
862-1055

County Offices

Belknap County
Laconia, 524-1737

Carroll County
Conway, 447-5922

Cheshire County
Keene, 352-4550

Coos County
Lancaster, 788-4961

Grafton County
Woodsville, 787-6944

Hillsborough County
Milford, 673-2510

Merrimack County
Boscawen, 235-5505

Rockingham County
Epping, 679-5616

Strafford County
Dover, 749-4445

Sullivan County
Newport, 863-9200

Private Agencies

New Hampshire Wildlife Federation

54 Portsmouth Street
Concord, NH 03301
224-5953

The NH Wildlife Federation is dedicated to the wise use, conservation, aesthetic appreciation, and restoration of wildlife and other natural resources, and to the protection of the rights and interests of sportsmenan and women. Of interest to you is the Federation's publication *New Hampshire Wildlife*.

New Hampshire Arborists Association

45 Elwyn Road
Portsmouth, NH 03801
431-6774

The NH Arborists Association organizes informational programs open to anyone interested in arborculture, urban forestry, and shade tree evaluation, maintenance, and horticulture.

Audubon Society of New Hampshire

PO Box 528-B
3 Silk Farm Road
Concord, NH 03302-0516
224-9909

The Audubon Society of New Hampshire conducts active programs in land preservation, environmental education, legislative action, and non-game wildlife.

Society for the Protection of New Hampshire Forests
54 Portsmouth Street
Concord, NH 03301
224-9945

The Forest Society is devoted to the wise use of the state's natural resources. Through innnovative programs in land protection, forest management, resource education, and advocacy, the Forest Society provides landowners with information and representation. It is the state's oldest and largest conservation organization.

This listing was adapted in part from a directory compiled by the University of New Hampshire Cooperative Extension office.

Appendix H
Selected Instructional Resources

The opportunities for developing schoolyard habitats are so diverse, we could not include all possible resources here. The emphasis in this listing is on wildlife habitat. For additional resources and information, check the bibliographies of the publications listed here. Also explore the internet for the many websites that feature schoolyard habitats, their development and use in education and as play spaces.

WILDLIFE STUDY
GENERAL

American Wildlife and Plants: A Guide to Wildlife Food Habits
Martin, Alexander C., Herbert S. Zim and Arnold L. Nelson, 1951
> How birds and mammals make use of trees, shrubs, weeds. Index cross-referenced to wildlife species and vegetation types.
Dover Publications, Inc., 180 Varick Street, New York, NY 10014

The Field Guide to Wildlife Habitats of the Eastern United States
The Field Guide to Wildlife Habitats of the Western United States
Benyus, Janine M., 1989
> Two excellent and readable guides, very accessible. Include definition of habitat, observation tips, and profile of each habitat, with charts, illustrations, maps, and keys, and specific information on individual species. 336 pp. each
Fireside Books, Simon and Schuster Building, Rockefeller Center, 1230 Avenue of the Americas, New York, NY 10020

Handbook of Nature Study, 24th ed.
Comstock, Anna Botsford, 1939
> About 700 separate natural subjects thoroughly discussed. Bibliographies. (middle and upper levels)
Comstock Publishing Associates, available from Central Maine Power Company, Edison Drive, Augusta ME 04330

Living with Wildlife: How to Enjoy, Cope with, and Protect North America's Wild Creatures around Your Home and Theirs
Landau, Diana and Shelley Stump, 1994
> This practical handbook contains wildlife conservation history; chapters on enhancing your grounds; a reference guide for identifying needs and habits of many species; wildlife problems; and resource appendices. 342 pp.
The California Center for Wildlife; Sierra Club Books, San Francisco
ISBN 0-87156-547-1

New England Wildlife: Habitat, Natural History and Distribution
DeGraaf, Richard M. and Deborah D. Rudis, rev. 1998
   Natural history reference. Includes discussion of habitat features.
   One page devoted to each species included, with illustration and map.
   491 pp.
USDA General Technical Report NE-108, Northeastern Forest Experiment
Station
Note: This excellent reference may be difficult to locate. See your local
library, Extension Office, county forester, or regional biologist for a copy.

Small Creatures — Examining Your Environment
Couchman, J.K., et al, 1974
   A wide variety of activities about the small creatures that live in your
   neighborhood and around your school.
Winston Press, Mine Publications, Inc., 25 Groveland Terrace, Minneapolis,
MN, 55403

AMPHIBIANS AND REPTILES

Amphibians and Reptiles of New England
DeGraaf, Richard, and Deborah Rudis, 1983
   University of Massachusetts Press, Amherst, MA

The Amphibians and Reptiles of New Hampshire
Taylor, Dr. James, 1993
   An easy-to-use field guide and species profile, the first definitive
   guide to locating and identifying herps in the Granite State. Includes
   extensive natural history description on each species, individual maps
   documenting distribution and sightings, complete keys and a section
   for recording and reporting your own sightings.
$6.95 plus shipping, Nongame and Endangered Wildlife Program, New Hamp-
shire Fish and Game Dept., 2 Hazen Drive, Concord, NH, 03301

A Field Guide to Reptiles and Amphibians of Eastern and Central
North America
Conant, Roger, 1975
Houghton Mifflin, Co., Boston, MA

Stokes Guide to Amphibians and Reptiles

Tyning, Thomas F., 1990

> Based on Tyning's extensive field work and personal knowledge of the subject. Thirty-two species are covered in the unique behavior-watching approach of the Stokes Nature Guides. Includes traits and behaviors to observe, and a quick reference chart for each species, enhanced by pencil sketches, and an introductory section on each group.

Little, Brown, and Co., Boston, MA

BIRDS

The Audubon Society Guide to Attracting Birds

Kress, Stephen W., 1985

> Useful appendices include listings of publications available in each state.

Charles Scribner's Sons, New York, NY

The Backyard Bird Watcher

Harrison, George H., 1979

> Examples of backyard wildlife habitats. 284 pp.

Simon and Schuster, New York, NY

The Bird Feeder Book

Stokes, Donald and Lillian, 1987

Little, Brown, and Co., Boston, MA

Birds - Examining Your Environment

MacBean, J.C., et al., 1971

> Activities specifically designed to get you involved with birds in their natural environment.

Mine Publications, Inc., 25 Groveland Terrace, Minneapolis, MN 55403

Cavity Nesters of North America

Scott, Virgil E., Keith E. Evans, David R. Patton, Charles P. Stone

Agriculture Handbook No. 511, Forest Service, US Dept. of Agriculture, Superintendent of Documents, US Government Printing Office, Washington DC 20402.

A Complete Guide to Bird Feeding

Dennis, John V., 1975

Alfred A. Knopf, Inc., New York, NY

Field Guide to the Birds of North America
Scot, S.L. and L.M. Swinson, eds., 1989
National Geographic Society, Washington, D.C.

A Guide to the Behavior of Common Birds
Stokes, Donald W,. 1979
Little, Brown, and Co., Boston, MA

A Guide to Bird Behavior, Volume II
Stokes, Donald W. and Lillian Q. Stokes, 1983
Little, Brown, and Co., Boston, MA.

Thirty Birds that will Build in Bird Houses
Layton, R.B., 1977
Nature Book Publishers, Jackson, Mississippi

INSECTS AND SPIDERS

The Audubon Society Handbook for Butterfly Watchers
Pyle, Robert Michael, 1984
Charles Scribner's Sons, New York, NY

The Bug Book: Harmless Insect Controls
Philbrick, John and Helen, 1974
Garden Way Publishing, Charlotte, VT

A Guide to Spiders and Their Kin
Levi, Herbert W. and Lorna A. Levi, 1968
Western Publishing Company, Inc.

Teen International Entomology Group (TIEG)
      An inexpensive periodical on insects.
*Cooperative Extension Service, USDA, Michigan State Univerity, Dept. of
Entomology, East Lansing, MI, 48842*

MAMMALS

Animal Tracks of North America
      Actual-size tracks of North American animals from chipmunk to
      "Big Foot" printed on heavy parchment paper. Suitable for display
      or for use in the field.
DeLorme Publishing Company, PO Box 298CT, Freeport, ME 04032

Wild Mammals of New England (Field Guide Edition)

Godin, Alfred J., 1983

> Describes the 100 species of wild mammals found in New England. Maps show distribution, and the text provides information on the ecology and behavior of each mammal. Detailed pencil drawings. This field guide edition is a condensed and simplified version of Godin's original scholarly work.

DeLorme Publishing Co., PO Box 298CT, Freeport, ME, 04032

PLANTS

Care of Wild Apple Trees

Olson, D. and C. Langer

USDA Forest Service, Northeastern Area State and Private Forestry, Broomall, PA

Conservation Plants for the Northeast

Lorez, D.G., C.W. Sharp, and J.D. Rufner, 1989

> Program Aid No. 1154., 40 pp.

Soil Conservation Service, US Dept. of Agriculture, Washington, D.C.

Growing and Propagating Wild Flowers

Phillips, Harry R., 1985

The University of North Carolina Press, Chapel Hill, NC

Native trees, shrubs, and vines for urban and rural America: a planting design manual for environmental designers

Hightshoe, G.L. 1987

> This is a comprehensive book on native species plantings in the U.S. An easy-to-use coding system guides the user in immediately finding habitat and climate requirements, wildlife value, and other parameters. It may be available through landscape design firms and schools or in larger college libraries. 819 pp.

Van Nostrand Reinhold, New York, NY

Shrubs and Vines for Northeastern Wildlife

Gill, John D. and William M. Healy, 1974

> Reference book for 100 species in 36 genera (all but three species are native.) Covers range, habitat, life history, use by wildlife, propogation, and management. Useful for researching specific species. 180 pages.

USDA Forest Service General Technical Report NE-9, produced by the Northeastern Forest Experiment Station with the Northeastern Deer Study Group, 6816 Market Street, Upper Darby, PA 19082

Spring Wildflowers of New England
Dwelley, Marilyn, 1977
Down East Books, PO Box 679, Camden, ME 04843

Summer and Fall Wildflowers of New England
Dwelley, Marilyn, 1977
Down East Books, PO Box 679, Camden, ME 04843

Theme Gardens
Damrosch, Barbara, 1982
> See chapters on butterfly and hummingbird gardens.
Workman Publishing, New York, NY

Trees, Shrubs, and Vines for Attracting Birds
DeGraaf, Richard M. and Gretchin M. Witman. 1979
> 194 pp.
University of Massachusetts Press, Amherst, MA

Wild Edible Plants of New England: A Field Guide, Including Poisonous Plants often Encountered
Richardson, Joan, 1981
> Fully illustrated field guide gives all the information you need to forage for edible plants. Thirty-two pages of color photographs and numerous botanical drawings make it easy to identify the 200 species of plants described. The text also provides information about identification, offers precautions about poisonous or potentially dangerous plants, and gives suggestions on picking, preparation, storage, and best use of each plant.
DeLorme Publishing Co., PO Box 298CT, Freeport, ME, 04032

FIELD GUIDES SERIES AND KEYS

The Audubon Field Guide Series
Alfred A. Knopf, Inc., New York, NY
Available in most bookstores.

Golden Nature Guides (all levels)
> Excellent sources of information for identification, classification, and connection of various species.
Western Publishing Co., Racine, WI
Available in most bookstores.

Nature Study Guild Keys
Watts, May Theilgaard, 1963
    Pocket-sized, easy to use guides for quick reference.
Master Tree Finder
Flower Finder
Winter Tree Finder
Tree Finder
Nature Study Guild Publishers, Box 972, Berkeley, CA 94701

The Peterson Field Guide Series
    The Peterson system of identification emphasizes visual differences
    and similarities rather than taxonomic relationships (although these
    are clearly indicated in the appendix).
Houghton Mifflin Company, Boston, MA
Available in most bookstores.

Pond Guide
Buller, Dave, 1975
    An illustrated guide for identifying organisms found in and around
    the pond.
Biology Instructional Strategies, University of California, available from
Delta Educational, Box M, Nashua, NH 03601

A Practical Guide for the Amateur Naturalist
Durrell, Gerald, with Lee Durrell, 1983
Alfred A. Knopf, New York, NY

WILDLIFE HABITAT ENHANCEMENT

The Backyard Naturalist
Tufts, Craig, 1988
    Simple, enjoyable guide on backyard habitat enhancement for the
    suburban resident; emphasis on birds. Includes some discussion and
    general tips with illustrations. 79 pp.
*National Wildlife Federation, 1400 16th St. NW, Washington, DC
20036-2266*

The Butterfly Book: An Easy Guide to Butterfly Gardening, Identification and Behavior
Stokes, Donald and Lillian, and Ernest Williams, 1991
    Includes over 140 color photographs of butterflies; two sample butterfly garden plans; complete lists of food plants; descriptions of the lives and behaviors of the most common North American species. Explains how to design a butterfly garden; how to identify any backyard butterfly, caterpillar, or pupa; butterfly metamorphosis; butterfly colorations and markings; how to raise butterflies at home. 96 pp.
Little, Brown, and Co., Boston
ISBN 0-316-81780-5

The Butterfly Garden
Telusky, Matthew, 1985
Harvard Common Press, Boston, MA

Butterfly Gardening
The Xerces Society and Smithsonian Institution, 1990
Sierra Club Books, San Francisco, CA

Enhancing Your Backyard Habitat for Wildlife
Picone, Peter M., 1995
    A practical reference booklet covering backyard habitat, food and cover, and habitat enhancement projects. Color photographs, charts, forms, diagrams, sample projects and site plans. Most applicable for the northeast. 27 pp.
Connecticut Dept. of Environmental Protection, Hartford, CT

Gardening with Wildlife Kit
National Wildlife Federation
    Official kit of the NWF Backyard Wildlife Habitat Program. Includes a 64-page overview for wildlife enhancement in backyards, plant lists, planning tools, bird feeding guide, wildlife gardener's journal, hummingbird feeder, and wildflower seeds. Attractive format with color photographs, details and diagrams, charts and instructions. Planning tools included are particularly useful.
National Wildlife Federation, 1400 16th St. NW, Washington, DC 20036-2266

A Guide to Urban Wildlife Management
Leedy, Daniel and Lowell Adams, 1984
    Good overview of wildlife in urban areas. Includes discussion of public attitudes, effects of urbanization on the land, wildlife adaptations to urbanized areas, and basic principles of management. 42 pp.
Urban Wildlife Resources, 5130 West Running Brook Rd., Columbia, MD 21044

Habitat Pacs
"Developed Lands - Restoring and Managing Wildlife Habitats" and "Urban Areas"
> These teacher kits include activity pages, lessons, posters, and other support materials.

Urban Wildlife Resources, 5130 West Running Brook Rd., Columbia, MD 21044

Landscaping for Wildlife
Henderson, Carrol, 1987
> May be the most comprehensive resource on the subject. Includes color photographs, diagrams, and appendices full of charts, project specifics, and materials sources. Covers rationale, basic principles, habitat components, and landscaping information for backyards, farms, and woodlands. 145 pp.

MN Dept of Natural Resources, 500 Lafayette Rd, Box 7, St. Paul, MN 55155-4007

Landscaping with Nature: Using Nature's Designs to Plan Your Yard
Cox, Jeff, 1991
> A landscape design book written with wildlife and nature in mind, aimed at the landowner. Includes chapters on water projects and plants for wildlife, as well as color photos, diagrams, charts and lists. 344 pp.

Rodale Press, Inc., 33 East Minor Street, Emmaus, Pennsylvania 18098

The National Wildlife Federation's Guide to Gardening for Wildlife
Tufts, Craig and Peter Loewer, 1995
Rodale Press, Emmaus, PA; 800/477-5560

The Natural Habitat Garden
Druse, Ken with Margaret Roach, 1994
> Ken Druse demonstrates how toanalyze habitats, their plant communities, and the smaller niches of a home site. Includes some 35 beautiful sample gardens, lists of native plants for each habitat type, and sources for local indigenous plants. 248 pp.

Clarkson Potter Publishers, New York
ISBN 0-517-58989-3

The Naturalist's Garden
Ernst, Ruth Shaw, 1987
> Written for the suburban landowner, for learning about and enjoying wildlife. Engaging, easy-reading, with information on creating a naturalist's garden, learning about nature through your "backyard nature center," and maintaining the garden. Covers all the basics and includes useful particulars like nest box dimensions, tree and flower charts. 272 pp.

Rodale Press, Inc., 33 East Minor Street, Emmaus, PA, 18098

New England Wildlife: Management of Forested Habitats (General Technical Report NE-144)
DeGraaf, Richard M., Mariko Yamasaki, William B. Leak, John W. Lanier
 Discussion of habitats and management methods, with habitat matrices correlating wildlife species with specific forest habitat types. 271 pp.
USDA, Forest Service, Superintendent of Documents, U.S. Government Printing Office, Washington, D.C. 20402

Urban Wildlife Manager's Notebooks
 This series of pamphlets covers natural history and practical construction information. Titles include "A Simple Backyard Pond", "Feeding Birds in Winter", "Rockpiles and Brushpiles", and others. 4-12 pp. each
Urban Wildlife Resources, 5130 West Running Brook Rd., Columbia, MD 21044

Water Gardening
Pesch, Barbara, ed., 1985
Brooklyn Botanic Garden Record, Plants and Gardens,
Handbook No. 106, Vol. 41, no. 1

Water Gardens
Stadelmann, Peter, 1992
 Expert advice and practical solutions for streams, pools and water gardens, with 150 color photographs. Technical aspects of setting up a pool are presented in drawings and detailed, easy-to-follow instructions. Also featured are photos of wetland and water plants, fish, and other pool animals. 145 pp.
English translation by Barron's Educational Series, Inc.
ISBN 0-8120-4928-4

WILD School Sites: A Guide to Preparing for Habitat Improvement Projects on School Grounds
Schiff, Paul and Dr. Cindi Smith-Walters, 1993
 This publication offers a rationale for taking action on the school site, a discussion of basic wildlife principles, and an outline of the steps in the process. Includes charts, checklists, and photographs, as well as information on WILD School Site Certification and the Project WILD Action Grant Program. 57 pp.
Project WILD, Western Regional Environmental Education Council, 4014 Chatham Lane, Houston,TX 77027

The Wildlife Gardener
Dennis, John V., 1985
Alfred A. Knopf, Inc., New York, NY

Wildlife Habitat Evaluation Handbook

Neilson, Edward Jr. and Delwin Benson, 1991

> This handbook, for use in 4-H wildlife management competition, covers management concepts, land regions, wildlife needs, and an index to 43 management (mostly large-scale) practices. Includes photographs, charts and mapping diagrams. Good for referencing specific material on some management practices. 130 pp.

National 4-H Council, 7100 CT Avenue, Chevy Chase, MD 20815

Wildlife Habitat Improvement Series

Langley, David, 1993

> A series of 3-5 page publications outlining the habitat improvement process for landowners, including "Identifying Goals", "Evaluating Habitat", and "Writing a Management Plan". Concise overview with illustrations and specific, practical instructions.

University of New Hampshire Cooperative Extension, Pettee Hall,
Durham, NH, 03824
ISBN 0-935989-71-4

Woodworking for Wildlife

Henderson, Carrol, second edition, 1992

> Discussion of 16 specific species (bird and mammal) which utilize nest boxes and platforms. Includes detailed woodworking plans and diagrams for construction of 24 projects, with photos. Plans for boxes for 46 species of birds and small mammals. 47 pp.

MN Dept of Natural Resources, code no. 9-14, 500 Lafayette Rd, Box 7 Cen-
tennial Bldg., St. Paul, MN 55155-4007

Your Backyard Wildlife Garden:
How to Attract and Identify Wildlife in Your Yard

Schneck, Marcus, 1992

> This book features over 200 wildlife visitors with information on habitat, feeding habits and nesting sites; includes over 340 color illustrations and photographs; lists the best flowers, grasses, trees and shrubs to plant to attract wildlife; includes examples of real wildlife gardens. 160 pp.

A Quarto Book; Rodale Press, Emmaus, PA
ISBN 0-87596-129-0

MAPPING AND SITE INVENTORY

Activities for Map and Compass Study (grades 4-6)
EE Series Bulletin 2471

> Teaches students how to use a compass, follow a course, and draw a map. Laid-out as a series of activities with instructional objectives, procedures, and materials. No illustrations. 11 pp.

Montgomery County Public Schools, Rockville, MD

Children's Special Places: Exploring the Role of Forts, Dens, and Bush Houses in Middle Childhood
Sobel, David, 1993

> Based on David Sobel's exploration and documentation of the natural interests of children at two very different sites (Devon, England and the island of Carriacou in the West Indies). Sobel supports his observations with relevant psychological theory, personal reflections, and descriptions of several wonderful educational projects. He calls for an "authentic curriculum" to address children's critical need to "find a place of their own." 170 pp.

Zephyr Press, Tuscon, Arizona
ISBN 0-913705-81-0

Connect, the Newsletter of Practical Science and Math for K-8 Teachers
May 1989 issue

> This 8-page newsletter includes the "Parish Maps Project" by David Sobel, and "Using Thinking Skills to Study Maps".

Teacher's Laboratory, Inc., PO Box 6480, Brattleboro, VT 05301,
single copies $3.00

Elementary Science Study (ESS) Mapping Teacher's Guide

> One of the best elementary science resources around. Focus is on map-making as the basis for map-reading. Illustrates diverse ways to get children involved in making 3-D, 2-D, topographical, classroom, and neighborhood maps with photographs of children's work and pictures of children's maps. Specific techniques for doing map and compass work, creating compass maps, and surveying the playground are all clearly explained.

Delta Educational, PO Box M, Nashua, NH 03061, order # 16-416-0353

Mapmaking with Children:
Sense of Place Education for the Elementary Years
Sobel, David, 1998

    This book presents an inspired alternative to the recitation and drill approach to geography education. David Sobel places the initial emphasis on local mapping projects that begin in students' own backyards and communities, and provide a sense of place. He identifies each stage of development, presenting relevant theoretical issues and several appropriate projects, with sections including "The Cartography of Childhood," "Mapmaking through the Grades," and "Exploring Hidden Landscapes." Vivid illustrations of the students' work are provided throughout to let you observe each stage of development. 166 pp.

Heinemann, 88 Post Road West, PO Box 5007, Westport, CT, 06881; 800/793-2154
ISBN 0-325-00042-5

Mapping Small Places — Examining Your Environment
Wentworth, Counchman, MacBean, and Stecher, 1972

    From the excellent (and out of print) series. One of the best curriculum guides to map-making with children ever published. Lavishly illustrated with color photographs of students at different ages in the map-making process, the guide suggests some wonderful projects. If you find this book, scoop it up!

    Some titles in the Examining Your Environment series are available upon request from:

Holt, Rinehart, Winston of Canada, Ltd., School Division, 55 Horner Avenue, Toronto, Canada M8Z 4X6

Mapstart, Vols. 1-3 (children's workbooks)
Catling, Simon, 1986

    A series of graded map skill and atlas books and related materials which gradually develop the basic skills children need to understand and actively use plans and maps of all kinds. Each with accompanying activity guide. Though content is British, Mapstarts is very valuable for elementary curricula in the U.S.

Collins-Longman Group., Ltd., Longman House, Burnt Mill, Harlow, Essex, England CM20 2JE

CHILDREN AND THE OUTDOOR CLASSROOM

Beyond the Classroom: Exploration of Schoolyard and Backyard
Charles E. Roth, Cleti Cervoni, Thomas Wellnitz, Elizabeth Arms, 1991
> Science activities at the elementary level (K-8) that require a minimal
> investment of time and equipment. 64 pp.

Order # 089, Massachusetts Audubon Society, Educational Resources, South
Great Road, Lincoln, MA 01773
ISBN 0-932691-10-2

The Curious Naturalist
Mitchell, John and the Massachusetts Audubon Society, 1980
> An illustrated seasonal guide to outdoor nature activities and natural
> history information.

Prentice-Hall, Inc., Englewood Cliffs, NJ 07632
ISBN 0-13-195404-0

Fundraising for School Grounds
Lucas, Bill and Anne Mountfield, 1995
> Includes how to manage school fundraising, useful fundraising
> techniques, how to obtain sponsorship, how to obtain grants and
> donations, useful case studies, specimen school grounds charity
> document, and color photographs. 68 pp.

Learning through Landscapes; distributed in North American by The Green Brick
Road, 8 Dumas Court, Don Mills, Ontario, M3A 2N2, Canada, 800/473-3638;

Geography in the School Grounds
Hare, Ralph, Christine Attenborogouh, and Trevor Day, 1996
> Topics covered include mapwork skills, use of photographs and
> models, weather, water and landforms, people, settlements and land
> uses, environmental quality, and sense of place; with real examples
> illustrated by color photographs. Suitable for urban and rural
> schools. Photocopiable worksheets. 72 pp.

Learning through Landscapes; distributed in North American by The Green Brick
Road, 8 Dumas Court, Don Mills, Ontario, M3A 2N2, Canada, 800/473-3638

The Great Outdoors: Restoring Children's Right to Play Outside
Rivkin, Mary S., 1995
> In this book, Mary Rivkin sounds the call for schools and
> communities to restore children's outdoor play opportunities, gives

inspiring examples of play spaces across the U.S. and the world, and offers practical ideas for bringing the great outdoors to your school. 106 pp.

National Association for the Education of Young Children, 1509 16th Street., N.W., Washington, D.C., 20036-1426, 800/424-2460 (order #108)

Hands-On Nature: Information and Activities for Exploring the Environment with Children

Lingelbach, Jenepher, 1986

"Idea book" of activities and concepts, covering adaptations, habitats, cycles, and designs of nature. Each section includes discussion of concepts with activities and follow-up. Covers lots of activities in a general, simplified way, with references for further, in-depth study. 233 pp.

Vermont Institute of Natural Science, Woodstock, VT 05091

Keepers of the Earth: Native American Stories and Environmental Activities for Children
Keepers of the Animals: Native American Stories and Environmental Activities for Children

Bruchac, Joseph and Michael Caduto, 1988 and 1991

Each story is followed by related activities that enhance and develop the concepts presented in the tale, as well as questions for study and ideas for discussion. All activities coded for easy reference. 200-260 pp

Fulcrum Publishing, 350 Indiana Street, Golden, CO 80401.
Tel: 303-277-1623

A Naturalist's Teaching Manual:
Activities and Ideas for Teaching Natural History

Wilson, Jennifer Bauer, 1986

The manual encompasses crafts, games, discovery trips, art projects, imaginative and creative endeavors, notebooks, experiments, and other ideas to guide the amateur and professsional naturalist alike in new and exciting ways to explore the natural world.

Phalarope Books, Prentice-Hall Press, Simon and Schuster, Inc., NY

Nature with Children of All Ages

Sisson, Edith A., 1982

Activities and adventures for exploring, learning, and enjoying the world around us. Fourteen chapters of easy-to-do activities requiring minimal materials, arranged by animal or plant group such as "Our feathered friends: Birds" and "Nature's life package: Seeds." 195 pp

Prentice Hall Press/A Division of Simon & Schuster, New York
ISBN 0-13-610436-3

Naturescope
National Wildlife Federation
> Wildlife information and activity books for children. Titles include: "Incredible Insects"; "Birds, Birds, Birds!""Amazing Mammals I & II"; "Reptiles & Amphibians"; "Trees are Terrific!" and others. Each offers multi-disciplinary activities with diagrams, photographs, and drawings. 60-70 pp. each

National Wildlife Federation, 1400 16th St. NW, Washington, DC 20036-2266

Project Learning Tree - Environmental Education Activity Guide, Pre-K through 8
American Forest Council, Second Edition 1993
> Many excellent activities intended to supplement existing curricula and arranged according to an overall conceptual framework.

Project Learning Tree, American Forest Foundation, 1111 19th St., N.W., Washington, DC 20036

Project WILD Activity Guide
Environmental Council for Education, second edition, 1992
> A collection of 113 activities, arranged by awareness and appreciation, diversity of wildlife values, ecological principles, management and conservation, people/ culture/ wildlife, trends/issues/ consequences, and responsible human actions.
> Each includes objectives, method, background, materials, procedure, extensions, and evaluation. Cross-referenced. 386 pp.

Project WILD, 707 Conservation Lane, Gaithersburg, MD 20878

Schoolyard Wildlife Activity Guide
Cronin-Jones, Linda, ed., 1992
> Includes outline of curriculum framework, relevant handbook entries, target audience, behavioral objectives, performance objectives, science process skills used, materials, best time of year for lesson, getting ready, procedure, and going further. Uses diagrams and illustrations. 208 pp.

Florida Game and Fresh Water Fish Commission, Nongame Education Coordinator, 620 S. Meridian Street, Tallahassee, FL 32399-9969

Sharing Nature with Children *(ISBN 0-916124-14-2)*
Sharing the Joy of Nature *(ISBN 0-916124-52-5*
Cornell, Joseph, 1979 and 1989
> Two pocket-sized, nature-awareness guidebooks for parents and teachers, with activities for all ages. Each game coded by concepts, mood, location, group size, age and materials. Emphasizes "flow-learning." Includes suggestions for teaching. 143 and 167 pp.

DAWN Publications, 14618 Tyler-Foote Road, Nevada City, CA 95959. Tel: 800-545-7475

Soil Conservation Topics Education Kit

> Activities on soil, water, and ecological resources, and soil and water conservation. Arranged by grade cluster (K-2, 3-4, 5-6). Each activity includes objective, materials, subject areas, introduction, procedure, suggested questions, supplemental activities. Accompanied by clear, copy-ready diagrams and activity pages. 90 pp

US Department of Agriculture, SCS, Fort Worth, TX

Special Places; Special People:
The Hidden Curriculum of School Grounds

Titman, Wendy, 1994

> A two year research project forms the basis of this publication. Using new methodology, the research identified how children "read" environments and how the messages and meanings conveyed by the design and management of schools grounds constitutes a "Hidden Curriculum". This book describes the research methodology and findings, explores some of the wider implications arising from the study, and suggests ways schools might effect change. Color photos from study sites. 140 pp.

World Wildlife Fund for Nature and Learning through Landscapes; distributed in North American by The Green Brick Road, 8 Dumas Court, Don Mills, Ontario, M3A 2N2, Canada, 800/473-3638

Strategies and Activities for Using Local Communities as Environmental Education Sites

Massachusetts Audubon Society

> More than 100 activities for exploring a community's natural and developed environments. 189 pp.

Order #059, Massachusetts Audubon Society, Educational Resources, South Great Road, Lincoln, MA 01773

Teaching Soil and Water Conservation: A Classroom and Field Guide

USDA, Soil Conservation Service, rev. 1986

> Twenty-two conservation activities with directions and interpretation, illustrations and photos. Activities to do in the classroom and compare with field observations. 30 pp.

Program Aid #341, USDA, SCS, Washington, D.C.

Ten Minute Field Trips: A Teacher's Guide to Using the Schoolgrounds for Environmental Studies
Russell, Helen Ross, second edition 1991
    An excellent guide with an introduction to each topic, suggested classroom activities, a section on teacher preparation, as well as a cross-referenced listing of field trips for hard-topped school grounds and an annotated list of supplementary materials. 163 pp.
$16.95 plus shipping (NSTA members 10% discount),
National Science Teachers Association, Publication Sales, 1742 Connecticut Avenue, N.W., Washington, D.C. 20009, Tel: 800-722-NSTA
ISBN 0-87355-098-6

Using the Environment: 4 Ways and Means
Trees
Minibeasts
    Environmental education books from England. Include specific hands-on activities for students to complete in the outdoors, with diagrams and illustrations. Some good material on mapping with children, identifying natural features, and making collections.
MacDonald Educational, 205 W. Highland Avenue, Milwaukee, WI 53203 (or Holywell House, Worship Street, London EC2A 2EN)

FILMS/SLIDES/VIDEOS

Contact your state wildlife agency for an up-to-date listing of offerings.

CHILDREN'S BOOKS AND PROJECT WILD

A 30-page file of children's books correlated with the material in the *Project WILD Activity Guide* is available from New Hampshire Fish and Game, 2 Hazen Drive, Concord, NH 03301. Contact your state wildlife agency.

Appendix I
Sources of Supplies

General Catalogue Listings
The Mailorder Association of Nurserymen
210 Cartwright Boulevard
Masapequa Park, NY 11762
("Gardening by Mail: Where to Buy It," send SASE)

National Gardening Association
180 Flynn Avenue
Burlington, VT 05401
(The National Gardening Association Directory of Seed and Nursery Catalogs, NGA members $3, nonmembers $4)

Rodale Organic Gardening
33 E. Minor Street
Emmaus, PA 18098
(Seed, Bulb and Nursery List, send SASE with 2 first-class stamps)

Bee Plants
Bee Pasture Seeds
RR 2
Sabetha, Kansas 66534

Bird Supplies
Bird 'n Hand Inc.
73 Sawyer Passway
Fitchburg, MA 01420

Droll Yankees, Inc.
Mill Road
Foster, RI 02825

Duncraft
33 Fisherville Road
Penacook, NH 03303

Hyde Bird Feeder Co.
56 Felton Street, PO Box 168
Waltham, MA 02254

Wells L. Bishop Co., Inc.
464 Pratt Street
Meriden, CT 06450

BIOCONTROLS FOR BUGS AND DISEASES

Gardens Alive!
5100 Schenley Place
Lawrenceburg, IN 47025
812/537-8650
(organic insect and disease controls, newsletter - catalogue)

Rodale's Organic Gardening Reader's Service
33 E. Minor Street
Emmaus, PA 18098
("Resources for Organic Pest Control" send SASE with two first-class
stamps)

EARTHWORMS

Cape Cod Worm Farm
30 Center Avenue
Buzzards Bay, MA 02532

Educational Supplies
DeLorme Publications Catalog
List includes many excellent maps, field guides, and wildlife prints.
Available from:

> **DeLorme Publishing Company**
> PO Box 298CT
> Freeport, ME 04032

ERIC Clearinghouse for Science, Mathematics, and Environmental Education
A current publications list and ordering information are available from:

> **SMEAC Information Reference Center**
> Ohio State University
> 1200 Chambers Road, 3rd Floor
> Columbus, OH 43212

GARDENING SUPPLIES AND TOOLS

Gardener's Supply Company
128 Intervale Road
Burlington, VT 05401

Green River Tools
Box 1919
Brattleboro, VT 05301

Walter F. Nicke
Box 667G
Hudson, NY 12534

ORGANIC FERTILIZERS AND SOIL AMENDMENTS

Garden's Alive!
5100 Schenley Place
Lawrenceburg, IN 47025
812/537-8650
(fertilizers, soil enhancers, newsletter - catalogue)

Rodale's Organic Gardening Reader's Service
33 E. Minor Street
Emmaus, PA 18098
("Soil Builders and Organic Fertilizers" listing; send SASE with two first-class stamps)

PLANTS FOR DIFFICULT CLIMATES

Garden City Seeds
Box 297
Victor, MT 59875

Johnny's Selected Seeds
310 Foss Hill Road
Albion, ME 04910

POOLS, PONDS AND WATER GARDENS

Lilypons Water Gardens
312 Flower Road, PO Box 10
Lilypons, MD 21727

Paradise Gardens
14 May Street
Whitman, MA 02382

William J. Tricker and Sons
74 Allendale Avenue, PO Box 398
Saddle River, NJ 07458

SEEDS, PLANTS, AND GARDEN CATALOGS

Caution: When ordering "native" species, find out the origin of the plants. If they originate more than 200 miles south, 100 miles north, or 250 miles east or west of your location, don't order them.

Botanic Garden Seed, Inc.
9 Wyckoff Street
Brooklyn, NY 11201
(Wildflowers)

Burpee Seed Company
300 Park Avenue
Warminster, PA 18991
(Fruit trees, shrubs, vegetables, flowers, wildflowers)

Conley's Garden Center
Boothbay Harbor, ME 04538
(Wildflowers)

Dutch Gardens, Inc.
PO Box 400
Montvale, NJ 07645
(Flower bulbs)

Garden in the Woods
Sudbury, MA
(Wild plants and stock)

Harris Seeds, Moreton Farm
3670 Buffalo Road
Rochester, NY 14624
(Vegetables, flowers, wildflowers)

Herbst Brothers Seedsmen, Inc.
1000 N. Main Street
Brewster, NY 10509

Kelly Brothers Nurseries, Inc.
Dansville, NY 14437
(Fruits, flowers, shrubs, trees)

JE Miller Nurseries
5060 West Lake Road
Canadaigua, NY 14424
(Fruits, trees, flowers)

Native Seeds
14590 Triadelphia Mill Drive
Dayton, MD 21036
(Wildflowers)

Pinetree Garden Seeds
New Gloucester, ME 04260
(Vegetables, flowers)

Putney Nursery
Putney, VT 05346
(Wildflowers)

Soil Conservation Society of America
7515 N.E. Ankeny Road
Ankeny, IA 50021
("Sources of Native Seeds and Plants" $3.00 postpaid)

Vermont Bean Seed Company
Garden Lane
Bosmoseen, VT 05732
(Vegetables, flowers, wildflowers)

The Vermont Wildflower Farm
PO Box 5, Route. 7
Charlotte, VT 05445
(Wildflowers)

White Flower Farm
Route 63
Litchfield, CT 06759-0050
(Flowers, wildflowers)

Material for this list excerpted or adapted from:

> *Landscaping for Wildlife*, Carrol Henderson
> *The Naturalist's Garden*, Ruth Shaw-Ernst
> Both books include more extensive listings of supplies, as well as
> other valuable information for enhancing wildlife habitat. Refer to
> the Instructional Resources list in Appendix H for more information.

Appendix J

Worksheets

On the following pages you will find a series of worksheets to assist you in developing and implementing your enhancement plan. Refer to the related chapters for discussion of these topics.

Worksheets Included:

Team Building Contact List (Chapter 1)

Wildlife and Habitat Inventory Form (Chapter 4)

Community Natural Resources Survey (Chapter 4)

Enhancement Plan Worksheet (Chapter 5)

Checklist for Action Projects (Chapter 6)

Maintenance Schedule (Chapter 7)

TEAM BUILDING CONTACT LIST

School Name: _____

Location: _____

Working Group – Core Team:

Contact Teacher: _____

Core Team of Students: (list class or individual names)

_____

_____

_____

_____

Working Group – Support Team:

Teacher Name_____ Grade _____

Teacher Name_____ Grade _____

Teacher Name_____ Grade _____

Teacher Name_____ Grade _____

Administrator(s)

Name _____ Title _____

Maintenance Staff Person(s):

Name _____ Title _____

Parent/Teacher Association contact:

Name _____

Board of Education contact:

Name _____

Advisory Committee:

Name _____ Contact Number _____

Association _____

Expertise _____

Name _____ Contact Number _____

Association _____

Expertise _____

Name _____ Contact Number _____
Association _____
Expertise _____

Name _____ Contact Number _____
Association _____
Expertise _____

Community Support Group:
(list parents, environmental professionals, local businesses, youth groups, service organizations, communications media)

Name _____ Contact Number _____
Association _____
Expertise _____

Name _____ Contact Number _____
Association _____
Expertise _____

Name _____ Contact Number _____
Association _____
Expertise _____

Name _____ Contact Number _____
Association _____
Expertise _____

Name _____ Contact Number _____
Association _____
Expertise _____

WILDLIFE AND HABITAT INVENTORY FORM

School Name _____
Size of Schoolyard Site _____
Size of Area for Project _____

Plants	Type/Species	Estimated Number
Large Trees		
Small Trees		
Shrubs		
Vines		
Grasses		
Annual Flowers		
Perennial Flowers		

Food	Type	Estimated Amount
Berries		
Mast		
Seeds		
Buds		
Nectar		
Worms		
Insects		
Other:		

Water	Yes	No	Type
Pond			
Pool			
Stream			
Spring			
Bird Bath			
Year-round Water Supply			
Place to Build Small Pond			
Other			

Cover	Yes	No	Type
Evergreen trees/shrubs			
Cavity/Den Trees			
Snag Trees			
Tall grass			
Rockpiles			
Rock walls			
Brushpiles			
Meadow			

Cover

	Yes	No	Type
Ground Cover	_____	_____	_____
Dens in Ground/Rock	_____	_____	_____
Pool/Pond	_____	_____	_____
Nest Boxes	_____	_____	_____
Other	_____	_____	_____

Other Characteristics

Sunlight — percentage of site receiving:

full sun _____ partial sun _____ shade _____

Temperature range

highest _____ lowest _____ average _____

Soil Type(s)

Soil Moisture - percentage of site that is:

very wet _____ wet _____ average _____ dry _____ very dry _____

Covered Areas – percentage of area covered by:

Trees and Shrubs _____

Grass Lawn _____

Recreation Fields _____

Buildings _____

Pavement _____

Other _____

Animals Identified
Mammals

Species	Type of Sign	Location	Estimated Number

Birds

Species	Type of Sign	Location	Estimated Number

Reptiles

Species	Type of Sign	Location	Estimated Number

Amphibians

Species	Type of Sign	Location	Estimated Number

Insects/Spiders/Invertebrates

Species	Type of Sign	Location	Estimated Number

Site Assessment:

What kind of soil type, sunlight, and climate conditions must plants be able to tolerate to thrive on this site?

Which areas of the site are best suited for school uses and needs? How should these areas be modified to make them more suitable or comfortable? Do they need screening or protection from sun, wind, or traffic?

Are there any areas of the schoolyard site that are not used for any activity, and could be replaced with wildlife habitat plantings?

What existing features can become a starting point for enhancing wildlife habitat?

What wildlife habitat resources are in short supply on your site: food, water, cover, space?

COMMUNITY NATURAL RESOURCES SURVEY

To see how your site fits into the larger picture, you will need to conduct a survey in your community. Such a survey should include information from the following areas (sample survey questions follow each heading):

History of the Community
1. How did your community get there and why?
2. What role did people/nature play in influencing the town's formation?
3. Interview older residents of the community about changes in the local environment during their lifetimes.
4. What are effects of all these changes on the community's natur and human resources?

Geography and Land Use
1. What is the town's shape and location? Why is the town shaped the way it is? Has it always been this shape?
2. How many people live in the community? Is it a part of a larger community or city?
3. How is the land used in the town?
4. Does the town have any serious land use problems, like erosion, landslides, or floods?

Geology and Climate
1. What is the geological history of the community?
2. Are there any special geological features? Do any geological features affect the town's climate?
3. What rocks and minerals are found in your community? Did they play a role in the development of the town?
4. Are there any laws on land management?

Animal and Plant Resources
1. What plants and animals are found in the community? Which are native and which have been introduced?
2. Are these plants and animals affected by the human community and its activities? Do the plants and animals affect the human community?
3. Are there any hunting, trapping or fishing laws? Are there any management areas?
4. Is there any "pest" control — rats, mosquitoes, other insects?

Energy Resources

1. What are the town's sources of energy - electrical, natural gas, propane, hydro, other?
2. Where does the energy come from? How is it made? Trace its route to your school.

Water Resources

1. What rivers, streams or lakes are located in or near the community?
2. Where do these bodies of water start from and flow to?
3. In the town, what is located along these bodies of water? Does anything happen to the water here?
4. Do a general inventory to find out what plants and animals are found in the water of your community. What is the pH, dissolved oxygen, etc.?

Water Supply and Use

1. What is the community's source of water? How is it treated?
2. How is water used in your community? Homes, schools, businesses?
3. How does the water leave the houses, industries, schools, etc.? Is it changed?
4. Is sewage treated? Where does it go?

Atmospheric Resources

1. Air
   What are the sources of air pollution that can be seen, heard or smelled?
   Locate and describe the source and type on a map of your community.
   What are the effects of air pollution on the community (wildlife, plants, people, buildings, water, etc.)?
2. Noise
   Where in the community are the sources of noise located?
   Is their location related to population density? Compare these sources of noise pollution with sources of air and water pollution. Are they the same? Different? What effect does the noise pollution have in the community?

Solid Wastes

1. How and where does your town dispose of its solid wastes (cans, metals, paper, food refuse, glass, plastic products)? Is this creating any problems?
2. Of the materials thrown away, which come from resources that can be restored? Which come from resources that can't be renewed? How could you reduce the amount of waste being produced?
3. Are there any recycling programs?

Industrial Aspects

1. What are the industries in the town?
2. What are the effects of the industries on the town and its resources?
3. What products are made by community industries? What are the steps in production?

General Questions about the Community

1. Who makes the plans for the way in which the town develops?
2. Who plans the use and management of water and air resources, land area developments, parks and open spaces?
3. What is the community's main source of income?
4. What are the conservation and environmental problems that are present in the town?
5. What conservation practices are and could be used in your community to improve its resource situation (reforestation, erosion control, soil conservation)?

Field Trips Associated with Community Natural Resources

1. Parks, sanctuaries, zoos.
2. Community solid waste disposal areas — incinerators, landfills
3. Industries.
4. Water and sewage treatment plants.
5. Power and energy utilities.
6. Areas of geological importance and interest.
7. Local water resources - lakes, streams.
8. Management areas (forest and wildlife).
9. Planning and zoning board meetings.
10. Conservation and environmental commissions.

Adapted with permission from Jerry Schierloh, Associate Professor of Environmental Studies, New Jersey School of Conservation, for Graduate Course "Outdoor Teaching Sites for Environmental Education," Montclair State College

ENHANCEMENT PLAN WORKSHEET

1. School Name _____

Address _____

2. Purpose Statement

_____

_____

_____

3. Working Team (Team Building Contact List worksheet attached)

Primary Teachers Involved:

Teacher _____ Grade _____ Subject _____

Teacher _____ Grade _____ Subject _____

Teacher _____ Grade _____ Subject _____

Teacher _____ Grade _____ Subject _____

4. General Site Description

_____

_____

_____

_____

5. Map of School Site (attached)

6. Results of Site Inventory

(Wildlife and Habitat Inventory worksheet attached)

General Statement:

_____

_____

_____

_____

7. Goals and Objectives

Goal: _____

Objectives: _____

_____

Goal: _____

Objectives: _____

_____

Goal: _____

Objectives: _____

_____

Goal: _____

Objectives: _____

_____

8. Enhancement Projects
(Checklist for Action Projects worksheet attached)
General List:

_____

_____

_____

_____

_____

_____

_____

_____

_____

9. Timeline
1-year Plan (attached)
5-year Overview

_____

_____

_____

_____

_____

_____

_____

_____

_____

10. Resources

Source/Donor	Item(s)	Contact Number	Contact Date	Rec'd

11. Maintenance Plan

(Maintenance Schedule worksheet attached)
General Maintenance Overview:

_____

_____

_____

_____

_____

_____

_____

_____

_____

_____

_____

12. Evaluation Method(s)

_____

_____

_____

_____

_____

_____

_____

_____

_____

_____

CHECKLIST FOR ACTION PROJECTS

1. Food - Feeding Stations and Plantings

Plants on your site which currently provide wildlife foods (seeds, mast, berries, buds, nectar):

Large trees	Number	Small trees	Number

Shrubs	Number	Annuals & Perennials	Number

Food Plots	Type	Number	Container Gardens	Type	Number

List the type and number of feeders and foods you will provide for wildlife.

Feeder Type	Number	Foods	Wildlife Species Benefited

2. Water - Drinking and Bathing

Type of water sources	Annual	Seasonal
Bird Bath		
Dripping Water		
Spring		
Wildlife Pool		
Pond		
Stream		
Other		

3. Cover - Places to Hide

Habitat Component	Type	Wildlife Species Benefited
Dense Shrubs	_____	_____
Evergreens	_____	_____
Cavity Trees	_____	_____
Snag Trees	_____	_____
Brush Piles	_____	_____
Rock Piles	_____	_____
Ground Covers	_____	_____
Meadow	_____	_____
Other	_____	_____

Cover - Places to Raise Young

Habitat Component	Type	Wildlife Species Benefited
Mature Trees	_____	_____
Small Trees	_____	_____
Shrub Tasses	_____	_____
Den/cavity Trees	_____	_____
Snags	_____	_____
Meadow	_____	_____
Nesting Boxes	_____	_____
Other Plants	_____	_____
Wildlife Pool/Pond	_____	_____

4. Other Projects

Creating Openings and Edges _____

Releasing Wild Apple Trees _____

Meadows_____

Other _____

Healthy environment practices:

Check those that apply to your plan:

_____ Eliminate most turf grasses.

_____ Conserve water.

_____ Rely on natural pest control.

_____ Use less commercial fertilizer.

_____ Recycle leaves, prunings, clippings, etc.

_____ Compost food wastes.

_____ Grow native plants.

_____ Other

MAINTENANCE SCHEDULE

Seasonal Tasks

Task	Who Responsible	Date to be Done	Initial Completed

Monthly Tasks

Task	Who Responsible	Date to be Done	Initial Completed

Weekly Tasks

Task	Who Responsible	Date to be Done	Initial Completed

Ongoing Maintenance as Needed

Task	Who Responsible	Date to be Done	Initial Completed

Appendix K
The Outdoor Classroom: Activities and Ideas

The activities included here are reprinted from nationally-available outdoor activity guides, most of which are available from your local bookstore. Sample these activities to decide which to include in your classroom collection. Information on how to access copies directly from the publishing agency is included in Appendix H.

In addition, we've included three sample calendars, suggesting seasonal concepts for study in the outdoor classroom. Use them as a reference to create a calendar tailored to your particular area.

AN ACTIVITY SAMPLER - SOURCES:

Beyond the Classroom: Exploration of Schoolyard and Backyard
Charles E. Roth, Cleti Cervoni, Thomas Wellnitz, Elizabeth Arms

> 33 science activities at the elementary level (K-8) that require a minimal investment in time and equipment. Divided by Life Science, Earth Science, and Physical Science. Developed by Massachusetts Audubon Society staff as part of the Schoolgrounds Science Workshops. 64 pp

Hands-On Nature: Information and Activities for Exploring the Environment with Children
Jenepher Lingelbach

> Idea book of activities and concepts, covering adaptations, habitats, cycles, and designs of nature. Each section includes a discussion of concepts with activities and follow-up. Covers lots of activities in a general, simplified way, with references for further, in-depth study. 233 pp

Keepers of the Earth
Keepers of the Animals
Joseph Bruchac and Michael Caduto

> A unique combination of Native American stories and environmental activities for children. Each story is followed by related activities that enhance and develop the concepts presented in the tale, as well as questions for study and ideas for discussion. All activities coded for easy reference. 200-260 pp

Nature with Children of All Ages: Activities and Adventures for Exploring, Learning, and Enjoying the World Around Us
Edith A. Sisson

> Chapters arranged by subject area (green plants, birds, water, etc.) with background information, activities adaptable to different age groups, and bibliography for each. Materials needed are simple, inexpensive, easy-to-obtain. Includes tips and techniques for teaching out-of-doors. 195 pp

Naturescope
National Wildlife Federation

> Wildlife information and activity books for children. Include multi-disciplinary activities, diagrams, photographs, and drawings. Each issue explores a different topic: mammals, birds, wetlands, endangered species, etc. 60-70 pp. each

Project Learning Tree: Supplementary Activity Guide for Grades K-8
Project Learning Tree, American Forest Council

> Many activities about trees intended to supplement existing curricula, and arranged according to an overall conceptual framework.

Project WILD Activity Guide
Western Regional Environmental Education Council

> A collection of 113 activities, arranged by themes: awareness and appreciation, diversity of wildlife values, ecological principles, management and conservation, people/ culture/ wildlife, trends/issues/consequences, and responsible human actions. Each includes objectives, method, background, materials, procedure, extensions, and evaluation. Cross-referenced. (Aquatic activity guide also available — see Instructional Resource list). 386 pp

Schoolyard Wildlife Activity Guide
Linda Cronin-Jones, ed.

> Includes outline of curriculum framework, relevant handbook entries, target audience, behavioral objectives, science process skills used, performance objectives, essential and supplemental materials, best time of year for lesson, getting ready, procedure, and going further. Uses diagrams and illustrations. 208 pp

Sharing Nature with Children
Sharing the Joy of Nature
Joseph Cornell

>   Two pocket-sized, nature-awareness guidebooks for parents and
>   teachers, with activities for all ages. Each game coded by concepts,
>   mood, location, group size, age, and materials. Emphasizes
>   "flow-learning". Includes suggestions for teaching. 143-167 pp

Ten Minute Field Trips: A Teacher's Guide to Using the Schoolgrounds
for Environmental Studies
Helen Ross Russell

>   An excellent guide with an introduction to each topic, suggested
>   classroom activities, and a section on teacher preparation as well as a
>   cross-referenced listing of field trips for hard-topped schoolgrounds
>   and an annotated list of supplementary materials. 163 pp

✍ SEASONAL ACTIVITY CALENDARS

The following seasonal calendars excerpted with permission from:

Mitchell, John H. (ed), with the Massachusetts Audubon Society.

Curious Naturalist, Prentice-Hall, Inc., Englewood Cliffs, NJ, 1980

Science and Natural History Sourcebook. Bulletin 563, University of Maine Cooperative Extension, Orono, ME

Wildman, Edward F. *This Week Out of Doors: A Nature Calendar.* John Spencer, Inc., Chester, PA, 1955

"Things to Do", seasonal suggestions from Edward F. Wildman

January
Catch and observe some snow crystals on a dark surface.
Identify and list the evergreen trees near your school.

February
Why do winds blow? List the causes of weather.
List birds due to arrive in late February.

March
Choose a "noon shadow" that you can watch easily. Sketch it each clear day.
Build a blue bird box.
List migrating birds due the latter part of March. How do you recognize each?

April
Why do flowers have odor and color?
When is the chimney swift due? Tell a story about it.
Observe a toad. Why is it interesting? Why valuable?

A CALENDAR OF NATURAL EVENTS

MONTH	1st week	2nd week	3rd week	4th week
MARCH				Skunk cabbage well up. Blackbirds, robins and song sparrows have returned. Shoots of day lily up.
APRIL	Wood frogs call. Salamander migration. Mourning cloak butterflies. Red maples bloom in swamps. Pussy willows out.	Spring peepers call. Tree swallows return. Phoebes. Forsythia blooms.	Spring azure butterflies. Toads call. House wrens. Spicebush blooms.	Catbirds. Swifts and barn swallows. Birch catkins out. Quaker-ladies bloom.
MAY	Black-and-white warblers. Yellow-rumped warblers. Dogwoods flower. Shadbush out. Violets bloom.	Warbler migration. Rose-breasted grosbeaks. Tanagers. Columbine blooms. Bloodroot flowers in open woods.	Indigo buntings. Great crested flycatchers. Lilacs bloom. Dandelions out. Buttercups.	Wood pewees. Flycatchers. Apple trees flower. Canada mayflowers bloom.
JUNE	Young mammals leave nests. Wild geraniums and viburnums bloom.	First brood of young birds leave nests.	Ox-eye daisy. Orange hawkweed.	First cutting of hay. Day lily flowers. Partridgeberries. Lady's slipper.

Teachers' and Naturalists' Almanac of Maine

every month offers opportunities to teach concepts of nature

Fall

	Characteristics of Nature	Interrelationships in Nature	Changes in Nature	Values of Nature
September	Discover kinds of wild fruits and their uses in nature	Investigate nature's seed dispersal inventions	Research the mysteries of migration	Start a naturalist's log to record your observations of nature
October	Research why leaves change color	Discover the preparations animals make for the winter	Find out why the days grow shorter	Plan the best route for a scenic foliage tour in the local area
November	Discover Maine's landscape when the leaves are gone	Investigate galls, the wintering home of insects	Explore why animals change color in winter	Objectively look at issues related to hunting and trapping

SQUIRMING SOIL BUILDERS

Grades: 4-9   **Group Size:** pairs
Duration: 1-2 class periods
Skills: observation, data gathering, experimental manipu-
          lation, data analysis, hypothesis development

**MATERIALS/
SITE NEEDS**

Focus: This exercise helps develop concepts of adaptation, diversity, and interrelationships. It provides concrete experiences with a nonvertebrate animal that help make children see firsthand the various adaptations these creatures have made for successful living.

It helps if the children have had some prior experience handling other invertebrates such as insects. There may be some initial squeamishness among members of both sexes about handling live earthworms. Be patient, let curiosity and peer example overcome these resistances. Teasing of the reticent may occur. This is a good time for a lesson in human relations.

Procedure: First explore the unpaved part of the school yard for the presence of earthworms. These animals eat their way through the soil and excrete little pellets of soil around the entrance of their burrows. These pellets make little turrets at the entrance and are known as worm castings. (*Kids often call them worm castles.*) Worms also pull dead leaves into their burrows to eat. They may find some burrows with pieces of leaves protruding from them.

You may want to count the number of castings found in sample areas the size of an 8½″ x 11″ sheet of paper. The students can put down a sheet of paper, mark the corners with twigs, and then count all the castings within the marked area. Which parts of the school grounds have the highest amount of worm activity? Worms are very valuable because they mix organic material into the topsoil and aerate it with their tunneling. Where worm activity is high, the soil is in good shape.

Next collect some earthworms. First see what you can find looking in rotting plant material, under rocks, or under logs. If you don't find many, dig for them in places where the soil is rich and moist. (*If necessary, the teacher can have the students bring in enough worms from home so that each pair can have two or three, or the worms can be acquired from a fishing bait store.*) Stress to the students that earthworms need moist soil or they will dry out and may die if they are exposed to sun and dryness for long periods. Keep the study worms in moist conditions while the experiments are made.

Follow-up activities. Back in the classroom the children will work in pairs (*could also be singly or groups of 3-4*). Each group will

- tools for digging
- pans for soil
- magnifying lenses
- glass or clear plastic plate
- flashlight
- paper
- pencil
- ruler
- a place where you may dig such as a lawn or other worm habitat.

have two or three earthworms to observe. Students should observe the animals, answer the following questions, and follow the appropriate instructions.

1) Describe the earthworms' color, shape, and how they feel to you.

2) How long is the earthworm when fully extended? When contracted?

3) How can you tell the head end from the tail end?

4) Can you tell top from bottom? Try turning the worm over, what happens?

5) Gently run your finger over the bottom of the worm. What do you feel? Look at the worm with a magnifying lens. Can you see the bristles? These are called **setae (singular seta)**. What function do you think they serve?

6) Describe how the earthworm moves. How would you compare it to the movements of a snake?

7) Count the segments on the worm. These are the rings around the body. Do all your worms have the same number?

8) Look for the **clitellum**, a swollen saddlelike area. which segments does it cover? Is it the same for all the earthworms? The clitellum is used in the reproductive process of the worms. After mating it forms a cocoonlike structure for the eggs.

9) Worms have no eyes or ears, but they are sensitive to light and sound. Devise and do some experiments that illustrate that sensitivity.

10) Place an earthworm on a clear glass or plastic plate. Hold it up to strong light. Can you see the insides of the earthworm? Describe how it looks.

Once observations are completed, the earthworms should be released where their activities can continue to benefit the soil. Students might observe how long it takes released earthworms to burrow out of sight.

Make an observation container of a jar or narrow aquarium. Put in layers of fine sand and good loam soil. Add several earthworms; the exact number will depend on the size of the container. Keep the soil moist and cover the clear sides with black paper that can be easily removed for periodic examination. Try feeding the worms leaves of native trees. Which kinds do they prefer? Also try vegetables like celery, carrot tops, lettuce and also cereals, fruit peels, corn meal, bread crumbs, and coffee grounds. Do not overfeed them and do not let the food spoil.

Observe the worms tunneling. Keep alert for any baby worms that may appear. But most importantly keep track of what is happening to the layers of soil you put in. How long does it take for the worms to mix the soil?

OPENING FOR WASTES

SEGMENTS

SAC OF FERTILIZED EGGS WHICH IS SHED LATER AND THEN LEFT IN THE SOIL.

MOUTH

SETAE (BRISTLES)

From Beyond the Classroom: Exploration of Schoolyard and Backyard by Charles E. Roth, Cleti Cervoni, Thomas Wellnitz, Elizabeth Arms. Massachusetts Audubon Society, Lincoln, MA, 1991

GALLS

Small Homes for Tiny Creatures

The goldenrod stem has a lump
The willow twig sprouted a bump
Some rumor a tumor
But I think I'd sooner
Believe it some kind of a mump!

What are those odd swellings on some plants, the lumps and bumps on certain leaves? Look closely, perhaps they are galls. A gall is an abnormal growth of plant tissue produced by a stimulus external to the plant itself. Stated more simply, some substance injected into a plant causes that part of the plant to swell or grow in a particular pattern. It may be on the leaf, stem, flowerheads, stalk, or root, but it can develop only while that part of the plant is growing, which explains why galls usually form in the spring.

Galls come in many shapes: round, conical, kidney, disc, or spindle-shaped. Their textures vary greatly, too, from almost fluffy to papery or woody, and from smooth to sticky, hairy, bumpy, scaly, or ridged.

The purpose of a gall is to provide a home for a tiny creature. And what an incredible home it is, with its solid outer walls and constant food supply. Insects and sometimes mites are the chief tenants of galls during the immature stages of their lives. Besides producing food and shelter, the gall keeps its occupants comparatively safe from parasites and predators, and it protects them from drying out.

Exactly what initiates the gall growth on the plant is not clear. It appears to be a chemical substance either injected by the mother insect at the time she lays her eggs or secreted in the saliva of the **larvae** as they bore into the plant for shelter or begin eating it for food. Sometimes the adult female seems to start the process and her offspring, carrying precisely the same chemical, continue to stimulate the growth of the gall.

How galls form and grow on a plant is intriguing. The initial stimulant causes starch to convert to sugar, resulting in an excess of food material, which stimulates the plant cells to enlarge and/or multiply and the gall to grow. Usually the presence of a gall does not harm the host plant. Although galls grow on a great variety of plants, oaks are the most popular, claiming 800 of the 2000 kinds of American galls, followed by willows, poplars, plants that belong to the rose family, such as blackberries and raspberries, and finally composite plants such as goldenrods and asters.

Each gall-making insect produces a specific kind of gall and usually it grows on just one species of plant. Often, especially in winter, you can identify a plant by recognizing the gall that grows on it. The goldenrod ball gall offers a good example. It is an easily recognizable ball-shaped swelling on the goldenrod's stem, forming only on the Canada goldenrod (Solidago canadensis). This particular gall is caused by a small, brown-winged fly, Eurosta solidaginis.

The life cycle of the Eurosta solidaginis is quite typical and shows clearly why the formation of a gall is vital to this insect's survival. The female fly lays her eggs on the surface of the growing goldenrod stem in the spring. Sometime in June the eggs hatch and each young larva that bores successfully through the stem's outer wall causes a ball-shaped gall to form around it. In the fall the larva makes a tunnel through to the outermost layer of plant tissue to provide the route for the spring exodus as an adult, then retreats back to the center of the gall. Protected through the winter, it remains in its larval stage until it is time to transform in the spring to the **pupal** stage. When the pupal stage is complete in late spring, a balloon-like bladder forms on the front of the fly's head, which it inflates to push the end off the pupa case. It then crawls through the exit tunnel and batters through the final barrier of plant tissue by inflating and deflating the balloon, which is absorbed afterwards into the insect's head. The adult flies soon mate and the cycle begins again. Without the gall to protect the larva through the winter, it would perish and the species could not survive.

The interrelationship between animals and plants is evident throughout our environment, but nowhere is the dependency of animals on plants more dramatically illustrated than in galls.

Goldenrod Ball Gall

Suggested References:

Borror, Donald J., and Richard E. White. *A Field Guide to the Insects.* Boston, MA: Houghton Mifflin, 1970.

Brues, C. T. *Insects, Food and Ecology.* New York: Dover Publications, 1946.

Hutchins, Ross E. *Galls and Gall Insects.* New York: Dodd, Mead, 1969.

From Hands-On Nature: Information and Activities for Exploring the Environment with Children by Jennifer Lingelbach. Vermont Institute of Natural Science, Woodstock, VT. 1986

GALLS

Focus: *Some species of insects create remarkable habitats for themselves by causing specific kinds of plants to form galls around them.*

ACTIVITIES	MATERIALS
Initial Question: What is a gall?	

VIEW A VARIETY OF GALLS

Objective: To learn what galls are and to see the differences among a variety of galls.

Give a gall to each child to examine with a hand lens. Notice color, shape, size, texture, where it grows on the plant, whether there are holes in it. Children introduce their galls either by telling something special about them or by asking a question. Try to include these points in the discussion:

1) Galls are temporary habitats for insects or other tiny creatures.

2) Galls form when the right kind of insect injects a chemical into its host plant, which causes the plant tissue to grow.

3) Gall-making insects must choose the correct species of plant or the gall will not form.

4) Each kind of gall insect causes its own specific type of gall to form.

Materials:
- *a variety of galls* preferably one for each child
- *hand lenses*

TO EACH HIS OWN

Objective: To notice individual differences among look-alikes.

All children are given the same kind of gall (goldenrod ball galls work well). Tell the children to examine their galls carefully so they can distinguish their own from other galls. Put all the galls together in a pile. Have the children find their own galls and explain distinguishing features. Have them guess what's inside.

Materials:
- *galls* all the same kind; enough for each child

GALL FANTASY

Objective: To understand the life cycle of a gall insect by experiencing the passage of time inside a gall.

Explain to the children that you will read them a story in which they are the characters. They should listen and follow the directions, silently. Give them each a cracker, which they may not eat until directed to.

Materials:
- *Gall Fantasy,* p. 87
- *crackers* 1 for each child

GALL HUNT

Objective: To find as many galls as possible.

In small groups, search outdoors for galls growing on flowers, bushes, or trees. Look on leaves, stems, ends of twigs. If there are many specimens of each kind, one of each could be picked for display or further study. Check for exit holes, or invasion holes by other insects; sometimes it's hard to tell the difference.

Materials:
- *hand lenses*

GALL FANTASY

You are about to become tiny, defenseless creatures. Please, very quietly, get your jackets and find a place where you can be protected, but where you can easily hear my voice. Crouch, become as small as you can, put your jacket over your head and be very silent. Close your eyes.

It is fall now, the days are growing shorter and nights are cold. But you can't see the daylight nor feel the chill; you are snug in your gall home. You can eat, your food is all around you, warm and dry, you need only reach out to the nearest wall for food. *Eat*, rest, and *eat again*.

The leaves have fallen, beaten to the ground by gusty winds and pelting rains. You are safe and dry in your gall home. But you are alone and it is dark.

Autumn turns to winter. The snows have come, the ponds are iced, winter buries food for creatures like yourselves.

The sun is higher now, owls are nesting, streams are thawing, and you are growing bigger. Warmth, snow melting, sap running. You sleep your final sleep, deep inside your private gall. The time has come for you to change.

The days grow longer and warmer. Grass is green and flowers bloom. Your gall home is brown and dry. You feel an urge to stretch and move, stretch and move, and suddenly you are out of your gall, standing tall, soaking in the sunlight, drying your wings. You are an adult.

FOLLOW-UP ACTIVITIES

1. Keeping Galls
Encourage the children to store different kinds of galls in jars, covered with cheesecloth and with dampened cotton in them, to see what kind of insect emerges and when. Check similar galls in the wild and compare dates. Keep a record. Try to identify the galls and/or insects by using a guide.

2. I'm a Gall Insect
Have the children draw, or write a poem or short story about what it would be like to be a gall insect inside its home.

3. Paper Maché Galls
Make small or giant paper mache galls that the children can look into or actually climb into.

Skills
Science Process: Observing, Inferring, Communicating, Predicting, Comparing, Sorting and Classifying, Experimenting, Recording Data

Integrated Curriculum: Art, Drama, Reading, Writing, Language Arts, Math

Suggested Reading for Children:

Hutchins, Ross. *Galls and Gall Insects.* New York: Dodd, Mead, 1969. (o — informative, adult)

Nestor, William P. *Into Winter — Discovering A Season.* Boston, MA: Houghton Mifflin, 1982. (o — section on galls)

ACTIVITIES	MATERIALS
WHAT'S INSIDE **Objective:** To see what an amazing habitat a gall is and what lives inside, and to learn the life cycle of one gall insect. Each group of 5 or 6 should have a gall, a knife, and newspaper to work on. Look at the gall carefully. Is the exit hole visible? Cut the gall in half (an adult should do this for young children), and examine the halves to look for: • insect — in its grub-like larval stage • exit route — hold each half up to the light for easier inspection • how much of the gall's interior has been eaten by the host larva and how much by other insect invaders From the informational essay, describe the life cycle of the insect that makes the goldenrod ball gall. **Note:** Children may express legitimate concern about destroying the insects and their homes. Discuss this. Possible answers include: 1) we have cut open a kind that had many specimens; most remain growing where they belong; 2) scientific knowledge is often gained by examining live specimens and our knowledge helps us understand and respect each creature's place in the natural world.	• *goldenrod ball galls* (another kind if none available) • *knives* • *newspaper* • *hand lenses*

CHAPTER 8

•Tunka-shila, Grandfather Rock•

(Lakota [Sioux]—Great Plains)

The Lakota (Sioux) people say that in the beginning everything was in the mind of Wakan-Tanka. All things which were to be existed only as spirits. Those spirits moved about in space seeking a place to manifest themselves. They traveled until they reached the sun, but it was not a good place for creation to begin because it was too hot. Finally they came to the Earth, which was without life and covered with the great waters. There was no dry land at all for life to begin upon. But then, out of the waters, a great burning rock rose up. It made the dry land appear, and the clouds formed from the steam it created. Then the life on Earth could begin. So it is that the rock is called Tunka-shila, "Grandfather Rock," for it is the oldest one. Because of that, the rocks must be respected. In the sweat lodge, when the water strikes the heated stones and that mist rises once again, it brings back the moment of creation as the people in the lodge sing to Tunka-shila, the Grandfather, the old one.

In "Tunka-shila, Grandfather Rock," there is a great awareness of basic geological concepts. Grandfather Rock is burning when he rises up from beneath the oceans, just as rock from the depth of the Earth's crust that surfaces gradually or suddenly (as lava) is hot and cools to the surface temperature. Volcanoes are places where the Earth's crust is very thin and rock emerges dramatically during an eruption, along with steam, heat, ash and fire. As in this first story, science tells us that over four billion years ago the hot, molten rock of the Earth's crust gave off water vapor that formed clouds and rain.

•Old Man Coyote and the Rock•

(Pawnee—Great Plains)

Old Man Coyote was going along. It was quite a while since he had eaten and he was feeling cut in half by hunger. He came to the top of a hill and there he saw a big rock. Old Man Coyote took out his flint knife.

"Grandfather," Old Man Coyote said to the rock, "I give you this fine knife. Now help me in some way, because I am hungry."

Then Old Man Coyote went along further. He went over the top of the hill and there at the bottom was a buffalo that had just been killed.

"How lucky I am," Old Man Coyote said. "But how can I butcher this buffalo without a knife? Now where did I leave my knife?"

Then Old Man Coyote walked back up the hill until he came to the big rock where his knife still lay on the ground.

"You don't need this knife," he said to the big rock. Then he picked his flint knife up and ran back to where he had left the buffalo. Now, though, where there had been a freshly killed buffalo, there were only buffalo bones and the bones were very old and grey. Then, from behind him, Old Man Coyote heard a rumbling noise. He turned around and looked up. The big rock was rolling down the hill after him. GA-DA-RUM, GA-DA-RUM.

Old Man Coyote began to run. He ran and ran, but the stone still rumbled after him. GA-DA-RUM, GA-DA-RUM. Old Man Coyote ran until he came to a bear den.

"Help me," he called in to the bears.

The bears looked out and saw what was chasing Old Man Coyote. "We can't help you against Grandfather Rock," they said.

GA-DA-RUM, GA-DA-RUM. The big rock kept coming and Old Man Coyote kept running. Now he came to a cave where the mountain lions lived and he called out again.

"Help me," Old Man Coyote said. "I am about to be killed!"

The mountain lions looked out and saw what was after Old Man Coyote. "No," they said, "we can't help you if you have angered Grandfather Rock."

GA-DA-RUM, GA-DA-RUM. The big rock kept rumbling after Old Man Coyote and he kept running. Now he came to the place where a bull buffalo was grazing.

"Help me," Old Man Coyote yelled. "That big rock said it was going to kill all the buffalo. When I tried to stop it, it began to chase me."

The bull buffalo braced his legs and thrust his head out to stop the big rock. But the rock just brushed the bull buffalo aside and left him standing there dazed, with his horns bent and his head pushed back into his shoulders. To this day all buffalo are still like that.

GA-DA-RUM, GA-DA-RUM. The big rock kept rolling and Old Man Coyote kept running. But Old Man Coyote was getting tired now and the rock was getting closer. Then Old Man Coyote looked up and saw a nighthawk flying overhead.

"My friend," Old Man Coyote yelled up to the nighthawk, "this big rock that is chasing me said you are ugly. It said you have a wide mouth and your eyes are too big and your beak is all pinched up. I told it not to say that and it began to chase me."

The nighthawk heard what Old Man Coyote said and grew very angry. He called the other nighthawks. They began to swoop down and strike at the big rock with their beaks. Each time they struck the big rock a piece broke off and stopped rolling. GA-DA-RUM. The rock kept rolling and Old Man Coyote kept running, but now the rock was much smaller. The nighthawks continued to swoop down and break off pieces. Finally the big rock was nothing but small pebbles.

Old Man Coyote came up and looked at the little stones. "My, my," he said to the nighthawks, "Why did you wide-mouthed, big-eyed, pinch-beaked birds do that to my old friend?" Then Old Man Coyote laughed and started on his way again.

Now the nighthawks were very angry at Old Man Coyote. They gathered all of the pieces of the big rock and fanned them together with their wings. The next thing Old Man Coyote knew, he heard a familiar sound behind him again. GA-DA-RUM, GA-DA-RUM. He tried to run, but he was so tired now he could not get away. The big rock rolled right over him and flattened him out.

• KEEPERS OF THE EARTH •

MATERIALS: Story "Rock to Rock," pencils, crayons, paper, samples of the three basic rock types, Figure 8-1.

Rock Charades

ACTIVITY: Examine the three major types of rocks for differences in their physical properties. Discuss how each kind of rock forms. Pantomime the three kinds of rocks.

GOALS: Understand that there are three main kinds of rocks and that each kind has its own characteristic properties and process of formation.

AGE: Younger Children

PROCEDURE: Beforehand: Create diagrams of the basic structure of the three types of rocks: sedimentary, metamorphic and igneous.

Pass the rock samples around and talk about how each kind forms. Discuss the properties of each kind of rock. Have the children pick at the rocks with nails to see how hard or soft the rocks are.

Now display the diagrams showing the basic structure of the three types of rocks. Form the whole group into a circle and have them squeeze together to imitate the particles of a sedimentary rock that are stuck together. Divide the children into smaller groups of four each. Have each group "make" a metamorphic rock out of their bodies by imitating the way that kind of rock forms. Now have each small group "melt" and then harden to form an igneous rock.

MATERIALS: Samples of sedimentary rock with many pieces stuck together, usually in layers, metamorphic rock with minute, aligned crystals and igneous rock, a solid mass which may have large crystals; nails for picking at the rocks; diagrams showing how each rock type is structured.

Making Soil[2]

ACTIVITY: Discuss the ingredients of soil, how soil forms and its importance to life on Earth. Examine soil outdoors.

GOALS: Understand the five major components of soil and the process of soil formation. Be aware that the thin crust of topsoil on the Earth supports the plant life that in turn feeds the animals and makes continuing life possible.

AGE: Younger Children and Older Children

PROCEDURE: Prepare the soil by combining each of the ingredients in the large pan. Start with the rocks first and talk about weathering by ice, rain, wind and the sun's heat. As you add the other soil ingredients, discuss the role each plays in the life of the soil community. Emphasize the importance of soil for growing plants, which in turn feed animals. When your "soil" is prepared, show it to the group and ask whether they think it is real soil. Emphasize that soil development is a natural process that takes many years. Then use the activities listed at the end of this chapter to study soil outdoors.

MATERIALS: Spoon, large metal pan, soil ingredients: rocks (mineral), leaves and twigs (organic matter), water, air, clay models of living things such as worms, soil insects, etc.

Extending the Experience

• Study the soil life outside using hand lenses, small garden spades and collecting jars.

• Take the temperature at the soil surface and about six inches (15.2 centimeters) below. Record and discuss the reasons for the differences in these temperatures.

• Find a road cut or eroded river bank and create a vertical slice of soil with a shovel to study the three layers, which are called *horizons* (See Figure 8-2). The

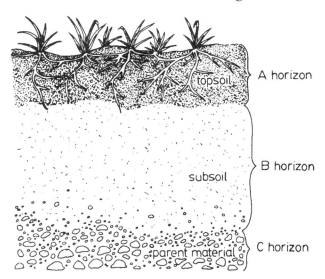

Figure 8-2. Soil profile. Topsoil is dark brown, rich in humus and other organic matter, and often well-aerated. It usually has a thin layer of partly decomposed plant and animal remains on the surface (A horizon). Subsoil is lighter in color than topsoil, has a high mineral content, is often colored by compounds leached from above and is a less favorable environment than topsoil for the growth of plant roots (B horizon). Parent material consists of rocks in various stages of weathering, which are usually derived from bedrock, and from which soil particles form (C horizon).

• Tunka-shila, Grandfather Rock •

A horizon is the rich, brown, organic *topsoil* which is high in humus and decomposing plants and animals. Below this is the *B horizon* or *subsoil,* which is lighter in color and often takes on hues from compounds leached down from above. Finally, the *C horizon* consists of rocks and other *parent material* from which the soil was derived, usually coming from the bedrock.

• Start a rock collection.

• Play rock friends. Have each child find a small rock of about 1 inch (2.5 centimeters) in diameter and have her or him get to know the rock very well by the feel of it, especially its shape, weight and texture. Each child should initial the rock to identify it. Collect the rocks in a hat or bag. The children must pick their own rocks out by the sense of feeling alone. Discourage peeking.

• Visit an area where rocks are abundant. Hand out cards with descriptive words such as rough, sharp, red, bumpy, smooth and heavy. Have the children collect rocks that fit these descriptions.

• Look at rocks under an ultraviolet light. Many rocks that look very dull in normal daylight, such as calcite, will glow under ultraviolet light.

Notes

1. The sweat lodge is a small structure where people gather in a cleansing ritual. The intense heat of the steam rising from heated stones purifies the body. This experience, along with the rituals of the "sweat," purifies the spirit.

2. See Chapter 16 for more information and activities about soil.

From Keepers of the Earth: Native American Stories and Environmental Activities for Children

by Joseph Bruchac and Michael Caduto. Fulcrum Publishing, Golden, CO. 1988

CHAPTER 10

❖ The Woman Who Married a Frog ❖

(Tlingit—Pacific Northwest)

There once was a young woman who was very proud. She was the daughter of the town chief and her family was very respected. Many of the young men wanted to marry her, but she thought none of them were good enough for her. One day, she was walking with her sister beside the big lake near their village. There were many frogs in that lake. A large number of them were sitting on a mud bank in the middle of the lake and she began to make fun of them.

"How ugly these frogs are," she said. Then she bent over and picked one up which was sitting on the muddy shore and looking up at her. "You are so ugly," she said to the frog. "Even another frog would not want to marry you!" Then she threw the frog back into the lake.

That night, when she stepped outside of her lodge to walk while the others were sleeping, she was surprised to see a young man standing there. His clothing was decorated with green beads and he seemed very handsome.

"I have come to marry you," the young man said. "Come with me to my father's house."

The young woman agreed. She thought she had never seen such a handsome man before and wanted to be his wife.

"We must climb the hill to go to my father's house," the young man said and he pointed toward the lake. They began to walk down toward the water, but it seemed to the young woman they were climbing a hill. When they reached the water they did not stop, but they went under.

The next day, her family noticed that she was missing. They searched for her everywhere and when they found her tracks leading to the water, they decided she had drowned. They beat the drums for a death feast. People cut their hair and blackened their faces and mourned.

One day, though, a man walked down by the lake. When he looked out toward its middle, he saw on the mud bank many frogs sitting there. There, in the midst of the frogs, was the chief's missing daughter. He began to wade in toward them, but they leaped into the water, taking the young woman with them.

The man went as quickly as he could to the chief's house. "I have seen your daughter," he said. "She has been taken by the frogs. I tried to reach her, but the Frog People took her with them under the water."

The young woman's father and mother went down to the lake. There they saw their daughter sitting on the mud bank surrounded by the Frog People. As before, when they tried to reach her, the frogs dove in and carried her under the lake with them. Then the chief's other daughter spoke.

"My sister insulted the frogs," she said, "that is why they have taken her."

The chief saw then what he must do. He made offerings of food on the surface of the water. The dishes floated out and then sank. But the frogs would not give up the young woman. They placed

robes of fine skins on the bank. The young woman and the Frog People came to the bank and took those robes, but when the chief came close, the Frog People drew her back into the lake. The frogs would not give her up. At last the chief made a plan. He gathered together all of the people in the village.

"We will dig a trench," he said. "We will drain away the water of the lake and rescue my daughter."

The people worked for a long time and the water began to drain away. The Frog People tried to fill the trench with mud, but they could not stop the water from flowing out. The frogs tried to drive the people away, but the people only picked the frogs up and dropped them back into the water. They were careful not to hurt any of the frogs, but they did not stop digging the trench. The water continued to flow out and the homes of the Frog People were being destroyed. At last the chief of the frogs decided. It was his son who had married the young woman.

"We are not strong enough to fight these humans," he said. "We must give my new daughter back to her people."

So they brought the young woman to the trench. Her father and mother saw her and they pulled her out. She was covered with mud and smelled like a frog. One frog leaped out of the water after her. It was the frog who had been her husband. But the people carefully picked him up and dropped him back into the lake.

They took the young woman home. For a long time she could only speak as a frog does, "Huh, Huh, Huh!" Finally she learned to speak like a human again.

"The frogs know our language," she told the people. "We must not talk badly about them."

From that day on, her people showed great respect to the frogs. They learned the songs that the woman brought from the Frog People and they used the frog as an emblem. They had learned a great lesson. They never forgot what happened to that young woman who was too proud. To this day, some people in that village still say when they hear the frogs singing in the lake, the frogs are telling their children this story, too.

DISCUSSION

"You are so ugly," says the young woman, "even another frog would not want to marry you!" This attitude of superiority over other life forms is common among human beings. It comes in such subtle, even cute expressions and story lines that we are often amused. It expresses a common belief that people are better than animals. Yet, the young woman's insulting comments in "The Woman Who Married a Frog" show that, by being too proud and not developing an eye for appreciating the animals around us, we can cause disharmony in the relationships between people and animals.

In the German fairy tale "The Frog Prince," a princess reluctantly keeps her promise and cares for a frog. Her act of kindness breaks a wicked spell and transforms the frog back into his real form as a handsome young prince. The young woman in this Tlingit story, however, pays for her

vanity by marrying a handsome young man who, in reality, turns out to be a frog! Then his relatives, the frogs, will not let her go.

But the chief and his people do not use force to rescue his daughter. First they make offerings of food to ask the frogs' forgiveness. Then they present robes of fine skins as gifts. All of these presents are taken by the Frog People but they will not give the chief back his daughter—the frogs do not seem to want to give her up. This brings disaster upon them when their home is drained by the chief and his people. Even though the frogs try to drive the people away, they are gently placed back in the lake. When the frogs finally return the woman to her people, she warns them not to speak ill of the frogs. In the end, the frogs earn the respect of these people and are even used as an emblem.

• The Woman Who Married a Frog •

If you are working with older children, have them draw pictures of a frog's or toad's tongue as it moves from the resting position, to catching its prey and back again. These pictures must show a gradual change in position, must be close to the same size on each card and must be drawn in the same place and position on each card. Figure 10-6 shows ten stages of the tongue in action. Ideally, children should create at least twenty sequential pictures including all of those shown in Figure 10-6 as well as the various stages of movement in between the stages shown in Figure 10-6.

With younger children, simply make copies of Figure 10-6, then have each child cut out the ten "frames" of the movie and paste each one of these onto a separate index card to create a complete sequential deck.

Once the illustrations are completed and placed in order, have the children hold one side of the illustrated deck of index cards tightly (or it can be stapled) and flip the cards in sequence using the open end of the stack. They will see a moving picture of a frog or toad tongue in action! Don't forget to tell them that this is how cartoons are made!

Amphibian Alert

ACTIVITY: Monitor and record amphibian sightings in your area. Take appropriate action for protecting local populations of amphibians.
GOALS: Acquire skills in observing and keeping field records of animal sightings. Realize the importance of records in monitoring animal populations over time. Understand how to respond to protect local amphibians.
AGE: Older children
MATERIALS: Chalk and chalkboard or felt-tipped markers and newsprint, topographic maps, transportation for the group, copies of the "Amphibian Watch" sheets (Figure 10-7), pencils, binoculars, hand lenses, thermometers, field identification and natural history guides to amphibians, flashlights, lined paper, tape recorder, tape of amphibians calling (available at natural history supply shops and bookstores), envelopes, stamps, other supplies as needed for additional projects that are undertaken.
PROCEDURE: Use the human impact section near the end of the "Discussion" section for this chapter as a springboard for exploring this issue with the children. Make an appointment to interview the appropriate naturalist, curator or other expert at a local Audubon society, natural history museum, environmental center or state or provincial nongame wildlife

agency. Prior to the interview, brainstorm with the children to generate a list of questions to ask the amphibian expert. Bring the children in to ask this amphibian expert some questions, such as inquiring about the status of amphibian populations in the area, certain species the children are interested in, publications in which to learn more and keep up with amphibian news, the location of important amphibian breeding grounds and actions that the children can take to preserve amphibians.

Use topographic maps to locate important amphibian habitat within a 1/2- to 1-mile (.8- to 1.6-kilometer) radius of the home or learning center. Use a larger radius if habitat is scarce. Before visiting the sites play some recordings of the amphibian calls they may expect to hear there. Lead seasonal field trips to these sites and have the children record their sightings using the "Amphibian Watch" sheets provided in Figure 10-7. Use the visits as exciting learning encounters to view and learn about local amphibians. Have the children send these records to a local conservation group or agency.

In some locations you will find breeding grounds where each spring, or during the wet season in arid regions, hundreds, perhaps thousands of amphibians emerge and migrate to breed. Lead a daytime or nighttime visit to this or these sites using binoculars, hand lenses and flashlights to observe the courtship and mating rituals. Some common explosive spring breeders are wood frogs, spring peepers and spotted salamanders. Countless numbers of amphibians are killed on roadways near these sites each spring. Work with local traffic authorities to set up a safe roadblock or traffic rerouting system on crucial mating nights. Help the children explore raising funds and environmental awareness to have some small tunnels installed under roadways where crucial amphibian crossings occur, as is done in some European and North American communities for toads.

Write to the World Wildlife Fund, Canadian Wildlife Federation, National Wildlife Federation, National Audubon Society and other private and government conservation groups for ideas on how to help amphibian populations throughout North America.[4] Compile a list of additional projects to get involved with using information and the children's own ideas.

EXTENDING THE EXPERIENCE

• *Collect Calls.* Listen to breeding amphibians calling and make up your own words, phrases and music that mimic those calls. Write down and/or record your phrases and songs.

House Hunting

Search for the best spot to build a nest and then try to build one.

Objectives:
Describe the nests of three common birds. Build a specific type of bird nest, using the same materials a bird would use.

Ages:
Primary and Intermediate

Materials:
- *copies of page 25*
- *bird research books*
- *slips of paper*
- *pencils*
- *nesting materials*

Subject:
Science

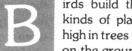Birds build their nests in all kinds of places. Some nest high in trees while others nest on the ground. Some plaster their nests on the sides of buildings or rocky cliffs and others build floating nests in marshy areas. Many birds also nest in tree cavities, stream banks, fields, and swamps. Birds also use a variety of nesting materials to build their nests, including sticks, mud, stones, lichens, grass, spider webs, snakeskins, and thistledown.

Some birds are adaptable nest builders. It seems they'll build their nests wherever they can find a spot and use whatever materials they can find. But other birds are much pickier and will build their nests only in certain places and use only certain materials.

In this activity, your kids can pick the perfect site to build a nest and then try to build one themselves. (Although most primary-age children can't do the research part of this activity, they can go on a hike to look for nests and good nesting sites, and try to build their own nests.) First write

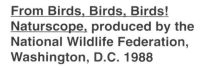
From Birds, Birds, Birds! Naturscope, produced by the National Wildlife Federation, Washington, D.C. 1988

down on slips of paper the names of five common birds that live in your area. (Choose birds that nest in your schoolyard or in a nearby park.) Divide the group into five teams and have each team pick one slip. Then explain that each team is a real estate agent hired by the bird on their slip of paper to find the perfect nest site.

Pass out copies of page 25 to each person. Explain that each person in the team must research their bird to fill out the nesting information sheet. (You can have them work in teams too.)

After everyone has filled out the information, take the group to a nearby park (or schoolyard or nature center) that has several different types of habitats. Have the kids in each team search for the perfect spot to build a nest. Remind them that most birds build their nests near a food source and that the nests are usually sheltered from rain, hot sun, and other types of weather. Also tell them that many birds hide their nests so predators can't spot them.

Give everyone 15 minutes to find the perfect spot and then have everyone gather back together. Start with one team and have the kids in the team describe their bird and its requirements for a home. Then visit the nest site and talk about the pros and cons of the location. (This one's too exposed, this one's too far from water, this one would get run over by a lawnmower, and so on.) After visiting all the nest sites for one type of bird, take a vote on which team found the best site.

Afterward, have each group work together to try to build the nest of their bird, using the same materials the bird would use. Each nest should also be the correct size and shape. Have everyone on the team pitch in to help gather the materials and shape the nest. (Warn the children not to pick flowers or pull living plants.) Then line up the nests and talk about each one. Encourage the children to look out for nests when they take walks with their parents or friends. But remind them that it's against the law to remove or damage a nest in the wild, even if it is old and abandoned.

do cotyledons help seed growth?

Materials: Bean seeds, cotton, water, six plates, six plastic bags.

Procedure: Soak the beans in water overnight. Place a layer of cotton on each plate and moisten it. Put several bean seeds on one plate as a control, and on the other plates place the following: embryos carefully removed from the seeds, seeds with one cotyledon removed, seeds with half a cotyledon removed, seeds with one and a half cotyledons removed, and several cotyledons. Label the contents of each plate. Put the plastic bags over them. Record results daily and find out how the cotyledons affect growth.

For another experiment, plant several bean seeds in soil. When the plants appear above the surface, remove two cotyledons from several, remove one cotyledon each from several others, and leave some seeds with both cotyledons as a control. Record results.

come-to-life gardens

Materials: Soils from different outside habitats in early spring, containers, water.

Procedure: Put the different soils into different containers. Keep them moist and watch to see what hidden seeds were in the soil that will now germinate and grow.

bean sprout sandwiches

Materials: Mung beans (or alfalfa seeds or other suitable seeds for sprouts), jar, cheesecloth, rubber band, water, strainer, bread, mayonnaise.

Procedure: Soak the beans in water overnight, and drain. Place them in the jar (it should be no more than half full) and put the

cheesecloth over the top, holding it in place with the rubber band. Keep the jar in a moderately warm place (65-75°F, or 19-24°C). Rinse the beans twice daily with water, draining all excess water through the cheesecloth. After four or five days the sprouts should be ready for eating. If desired, the sprouts may be put in a sunny window for the last day to develop chlorophyll.

Sprouts, mayonnaise, and bread are all that is needed for delicious sandwiches. Or, sample the sprouts plain with a touch of salt. Wouldn't this be a tasty ending to a study of seed growth?

seed dispersal activities

how do seeds travel?

Materials: Bags, or other containers for carrying seeds.

Procedure: Collect different seeds outside. Use observation and deduction to find out how each kind is dispersed. (Fall is the best time for this activity.)

Dispersal by parachute is simple to understand. The children have only to blow dandelion or milkweed seeds to see how the parachutes work. Helicopters are also easy. Toss maple, ash, or elm seeds in the air and watch how they descend. Children like to shake the little seeds from the pepper-shaker seed heads of iris, or touch the slingshot pods of jewelweed, also understandably known as touch-me-not. Perhaps during the seed hunt, someone will acquire some hitchhikers. Look on clothing for tick trefoil seeds, or burs of burdock or cocklebur; remove them, throw them away, and the method of dispersal is obvious. Eat apples on the hunt, throw the cores, and

TRAVELLING SEEDS –

Jewelweed

SLING SHOTS

Witch-Hazel

Bean

HELICOPTERS

Maple

Tree of Heaven

Linden

PARACHUTES

Dandelion

Sycamore

Milkweed

again the dispersal technique is obvious. Have the children think about what may happen to some of the indigestible seeds of fruits to help them understand dispersal by animal express. Tumbleweed seeds are tossed out as the old plant is blown by the wind; if you have tumbleweed in your area,

From **Nature with Children of All Ages** by Edith A. Sisson • Prentice Hall Press • A division of Simon & Schuster, NY, 1982

HITCH HIKERS

Burdock

Beggar-ticks

Tick Trefoil

ANIMAL EXPRESS

Cherries

and Berries

Poison Ivy

BOATS

Coconut

Cranberries

The Lotus pod rots, dropping seeds as it travels

MSS

inspect one for seeds and have the children figure out how they are dispersed. You may not find any boat-traveling seeds on your hunt; ask the children about coconuts and sea beans; some may know how they float like boats. Cranberries also float. Buy some later, and have the children cut

them open to see the air spaces that give them buoyancy. If you spot a squirrel on the hunt, ask the children what squirrels do with acorns, and they may understand how some oak trees are planted. After a seed-collecting hunt, children enjoy making seed-dispersal displays; most seeds can easily be stuck to paper with transparent tape.

milkweed seed classroom game

Materials: Two to four milkweed seeds.

Procedure: Ask everyone to remain seated. Release the milkweed seeds and see how long the students can keep the seeds in the air by blowing them up. (Using hands is not allowed; ask the students to sit on their hands to help them remember.)

fly parachutes & helicopters

Materials: Seeds that travel by parachute (milkweed, thistle) and helicopter (maple, ash, elm).

Procedure: Divide the class into two groups. One group goes outside by the school building. The other group goes to windows of an upstairs classroom and releases parachutes and helicopters. The students below try to catch them, usually with great enthusiasm and excitement. Let the groups change places and repeat the fun.

goldenrod parachute math

Materials: Several goldenrod plants with seed heads.

Procedure: Count the number of parachutelike seeds on one seed head. Count the number of seed heads on a spray, the number of sprays on a branch, and the number of fruiting branches on

the plant. Multiply these numbers to find an estimate of the number of seeds produced by one plant. Repeat the process with several other plants to compute an average number per plant.

Calculate how much land would be needed if all the seeds of one goldenrod plant were to germinate and grow. If 1 square foot (.9 sq. m) is allowed for each two seeds, the average number of seeds per plant must be divided by two to find the number of square feet (or meters) needed for all the seeds to grow. Find out the area of the school yard or grounds. Compute how many goldenrod plants would be needed to produce enough seeds to populate the whole area with these plants, assuming the impossible—that every seed will grow into a new plant.

Do this kind of exercise with other plants. Along with math, it teaches how prolific nature must be in order to ensure reproduction.

johnny appleseed

Materials: Books and other materials with information about Johnny Appleseed (also see bibliography at end of this chapter).

Procedure: Have the students do research on the role of Johnny Appleseed (born John Chapman in Massachusetts, 1775–1845) in dispersing apple seeds along the frontier.

Since the beginnings of agriculture, people have been important agents in seed dispersal. The colonists carried many seeds of familiar Old World plants with them to America, and many other seeds "hitchhiked" in hay, on the bottom of boots, and in other ways. Have the students do research on people as seed dispersers. The children can create a classroom play about Johnny Appleseed.

64 LOOKING AT LEAVES

LEVELS
Activity: Grades K-4
Enrichment: Grades PreK-8

SUBJECTS
Science, Visual Arts

CONCEPTS
■ Populations of organisms exhibit variations in size and structure as a result of their adaptation to their habitats. (10.1)

■ Biological diversity results from the interaction of living and non-living environmental components such as air, water, climate, and geologic features. (1.1)

SKILLS
Comparing and Contrasting, Classifying and Categorizing, Identifying Attributes and Components

OBJECTIVES
Students will ① describe how leaf shapes, sizes, and other characteristics vary from tree to tree and ② explain how particular types of trees can be identified by their leaves.

MATERIALS
Tree leaves, pencils, leaf print supplies for "Enrichment" (Types will vary depending on print method used; see various "Enrichment" activities.), copies of student page 231 (for assessment)

TIME CONSIDERATIONS
Preparation: 20 minutes

Activity: 50 minutes

<u>from the Project Learning Tree Activity Guide for Grades K-8</u> by the American Forest Council, Washington, D.C., revised 1993

Overview
Are leaves ever hairy? Do they have teeth? In this activity, your students will take a closer look at leaves and find out more about leaf characteristics and how leaves can be used to identify trees.

Background
See Background for "Name that Tree" on page 244.

Getting Ready
Locate an area where the students can collect leaves (from the ground, if possible) from several different kinds of trees. You may want to collect a sample, including needles from coniferous trees. In temperate climates, this activity is easiest to do in the fall.

Doing the Activity
1. Take students outside. Have them collect two or three different kinds of tree leaves, and encourage them to pick leaves that have already fallen to the ground. Be sure to collect needles in the clusters in which they grow.

2. When back inside, have students examine their leaves.

■ What are the differences between the leaves?

■ What do the leaves have in common?

■ Do any leaves have teeth?

■ Do any have hairs?

■ What do the leaves feel like?

■ Who found the biggest leaf? the narrowest leaf? the smallest leaf?

■ Have any leaves been eaten by insects? How can they tell?

■ Can they trace the veins on their leaves with their fingers?

If no one collected needles, pass out some that you collected earlier or show them a picture of needles. Have students compare the needles to the other leaves.

3. Have students give one of their leaves to another student. Explain that they will go outside to find what kind

of tree that leaf came from. How will they know when they've found the right tree? (It will have the same kind of leaves.)

4. Take students back to the same trees where they gathered leaves in Step 1. Walk from tree to tree, and have students compare their leaves with leaves on the tree. If one or more students has a leaf that matches a tree, stop and examine the tree more closely.

■ Where on the branch do leaves grow?

■ How are they attached?

■ Do the leaves grow far apart from each other, close together, or in clumps?

■ If the leaves are needle-like, how many needles are in each cluster?

■ Are all the clusters the same? Are all the needles in the cluster the same length?

■ Do all leaves on the tree match exactly?

■ What color are the leaves?

■ Also examine other characteristics of the tree. For example, what is the bark of the tree like?

■ What color is the bark?

■ Are flowers, nuts, or fruit on the tree? What do they look like?

5. Continue looking at trees until all students have identified the tree that their leaf came from. As they examine each tree, be sure to ask questions to make students compare trees that they've looked at. For example, ask:

■ Are this tree's leaves larger or smaller than the last tree's leaves?

- This tree's leaves grow in a clump. Have we looked at any other trees that have leaves which grow in a clump?

- What's similar or different about these two trees?

Enrichment—Leaf Art
Have students use the leaves they collected in Step 1 of "Doing the Activity" to create their own prints. Here are four "leafy" ideas for you to try, depending on the age of your students and the amount of time available.

Leaf Crayon Rubbings
Materials
Dark-colored crayons, plain drawing paper

Directions
Set the leaf on a smooth surface, preferably vein-side up; then cover it with a plain piece of paper. Rub a crayon sideways back and forth across the paper above the leaf. The margin of the leaf as well as its veins should begin to show on the paper as you rub gently.

Spatter Prints
Materials
9" x 12" (23 cm - 30 cm) wire, plastic, or nylon net screen; toothbrush; straight pins; tempera paint; paper

Directions
Place a leaf on a sheet of paper and secure it with pins. Then place the screen over the leaf and paint across the screen using a toothbrush. Afterward, lift off the screen, unpin the leaf, and carefully lift the leaf away.

Pressed Leaves
Materials
Iron, towel, wax paper

Directions
Place a leaf between two layers of wax paper and then cover with a towel. Press the towel with a warm iron, being sure to iron over the entire area of wax paper. (This will seal the leaf between the two layers of wax paper.) Afterward, you can cut out each leaf, leaving a narrow margin of wax paper around the entire edge of the leaf. Then you can punch holes through the wax paper at the top margin of the leaf and hang the pressed leaf. Use several leaves to make a hanging leaf mobile.

Leaf Print T-Shirts
Materials
Clean, poly-cotton-blend T-shirt; acrylic paints; paintbrush; piece of cardboard; wax paper; paper towels

Directions
Place the shirt on a clean, flat surface; then slide the cardboard between the front and back of the shirt to keep paint from soaking through. Place a leaf on a sheet of wax paper and coat it with a thin layer of paint. Make sure your fingers are clean; then carefully lift the painted leaf up and place it (painted side down) on the shirt. Cover the leaf with a paper towel and press it down. Lift the leaf straight off the shirt. Make as many more leaf prints on the shirt as you would like; then hang the shirt to dry.

NOTE—Do not use fabric softeners to clean or dry your shirt before you start printing. Also, to help make the prints last longer, rinse the finished shirt in a mild water and vinegar solution before washing it for the first time.

Cherokee Leaf Printing
Materials
A medium-sized, flat-headed hammer (a flat rock will also work); masking tape; a large, flat board; a supply of newspapers; wax paper; pieces of white cloth or clothing to print on (100% cotton or unbleached muslin works best); leaves from marigolds, tulip poplars, red or white oaks; carrot tops; strawberries.

Directions
The idea is to transfer the natural dyes from a leaf to a fabric, while retaining the design of the original leaf. Do this by beating the leaf's chlorophyll directly into the cloth, which will set the dye through natural chemical action. Use this technique to decorate any natural cloth surface such as table cloths, curtains, wall hangings, T-shirts, handkerchiefs, and headbands. Lay several thicknesses of newspaper on a flat board. Spread your cloth, right side up, on top of the newspaper. Put leaves on the cloth in a pattern of

your choice. Place wax paper over the leaves and tape it around the edges. Use a hammer to pound the leaf until the color transfers to the cloth. Pound evenly for a good print. If the leaf does not print evenly, crumple up another leaf, dip it water, and use it to "paint" the unstained spots. The dyes from the leaves must be set into the fabric to resist fading. This process also affects the color. For bright colors, soak the fabric in a solution of 3 tablespoons (44 ml) of ferrous sulfate per gallon (3.8 liter) of water for 1-2 minutes (or use the same solution of alum for a less-brilliant color set). For rich, reddish-brown hues, use a solution of 1 cup (240 ml) wood ashes to 3 gallons (11.3 l) of cold water for 5 minutes. Rinse the fabric in clean water, and air dry it away from direct sunlight. To help retain the natural colors, you can soak the finished piece in 1/2 cup (120 ml) of salt to 2 gallons (7.5 l) of water for 10 minutes [or in a solution of 3 tablespoons (44 ml) of baking soda to 1 gallon (3.8 l) of water]. Rinse and dry as directed above.

Leaf Batik

Materials:

100% cotton cloth squares, pencils or pens, yellow and/or orange fabric dye, red and/or brown dye, household paraffin, hot plate, heavy saucepan, metal spoons, natural bristle paintbrushes, large glass or metal bowls, clothesline and clothespin, leaves for tracing patterns, newspaper, glass cups or dishes for melted paraffin, iron, rubber gloves for students and adults.

Directions

Trace a leaf pattern onto a cloth square with pencil or pen. Using yellow and/or orange dyes only, dip each square in dye. Hang squares on the clothesline to dry. After they have dried, "paint" the leaf shape on the cloth with melted paraffin, filling in the outline of the leaf you have traced. Constantly reheat the paraffin; if it is not sufficiently heated, it will turn white (cool) immediately after being painted onto the fabric and will not protect the fibers from receiving the final dye color. Ask students what they think will happen when they dip the cloth into the next colors of dye. (The dye will affect only those areas not covered by the paraffin.) Crumple the prepared cloth, then dip it into the red and/or brown dye(s). Hang the cloth on the clothesline to dry. When it is dry, iron the cloth between layers of newspaper. Change the paper when it becomes saturated with paraffin. When no more paraffin melts onto the paper, the batik is finished. You might display the finished squares of cloth as a quilt.

END NOTES...

ASSESSMENT OPPORTUNITY

Pass out a copy of page 231 to all students, and tell them that they have to identify which tree each leaf on the right side of the page came from. Explain that they should use the tree drawings on the left side of the page to make identifications. As they identify the leaves, have students draw a line from leaf to tree and then copy the tree name onto the line next to the leaf. Afterward, have students explain how they identified each leaf.

RELATED ACTIVITIES

Name That Tree, The Closer You Look, Bursting Buds, The Shape of Things, Adopt a Tree

GRASSHOPPER GRAVITY!

OBJECTIVES

Students will: 1) describe a relationship between structure and function; 2) generalize that wildlife ranges from small to large and occurs in a variety of forms; and 3) recognize that people have power to affect other animals and with that power comes responsibility.

METHOD

Students observe, handle and describe live grasshoppers or crickets.

BACKGROUND

The major purpose of this activity is for students to recognize that wildlife occurs in a variety of forms and that people have power to affect animals. In the process of participating in this activity, students develop important observation skills—and an increased appreciation for grasshoppers!

MATERIALS

one plastic container; hand lens; live grasshopper or cricket for every two students; chalkboard

PROCEDURE

1. People don't often think of insects as animals and they hardly ever think of grasshoppers as wildlife. But a grasshopper is wildlife, too! Either send a small group of students out to collect grasshoppers in plastic

Age: Grades 2-7 (and older)
Subjects: Science, Language Arts, Social Studies
Skills: analysis, classification, comparing similarities and differences, computation, description, discussion, generalization, listing, observation, reading, writing
Duration: 45 minutes, or longer if all questions are used; can serve as basis for two-week unit of study
Group Size: any
Setting: outdoors and indoors
Conceptual Framework Reference: I.B.4, I.D., II.A.3., II.B., II.F
Key Vocabulary: wildlife, compound, antennae, appendage, estimate, habitat, responsibility
Appendices: Outdoors, Field Ethics, Animals in the Classroom

jars or send pairs of students out with a plastic jar. (A clear, plastic sheet pulled to the ground by two students usually traps grasshoppers safely!) You need one grasshopper for every two students. (Crickets can also be studied and can sometimes be purchased from pet and sporting goods stores.) Caution the students not to harm the grasshoppers. When you are through studying the grasshoppers, please release them. Tell the students they are going to be like some scientists who carefully observe wildlife with as little impact as possible on the animals. Be prepared, however, for an accidental mishap that a grasshopper doesn't survive. Deal with such accidents on a case-by-case basis, encouraging the students to be careful—but also not to feel guilty if a grasshopper accidentally dies.

2. The following questions may be written out in some form for the students to use in observing the grasshoppers, or you might offer questions to the students aloud as they examine the grasshoppers. (This list can be shortened, and different questions used.) You may want to define some of the vocabulary before using the questions—like antennae, appendage. (For older students, see "Wild Words—A Journal-Making Activity" that could precede this activity.)

3. Finally, remind the students that a grasshopper is only one kind of animal. Animals, including wildlife, are all sizes and shapes. Some are smaller than a grasshopper, and some—like the whale—are much, much bigger.

4. Ask the students to take the grasshoppers outside and let them go. Some of the students may want to keep the grasshoppers as pets. Talk with the students

GRASSHOPPERS!

INTERESTING FEATURES What are some of the most outstanding features of the grasshopper?

LEGS How many legs does it have? Are they alike or different? Which legs are the jumping legs? Notice where the legs are attached to the grasshopper's body.

WINGS Look at the wings, if they are present. (Adults have wings. Immature grasshoppers show pads or stumps.) How many wings are there? Notice where they attach to the body.

HEAD Look at the head. How many eyes do you see? Why do you think they have so many eyes? Do they look like your eyes? Check carefully in front and below the large, compound eyes for three smaller, simpler eyes. These eyes probably see light but may not be able to see shapes, sizes and colors.

MOUTH Do you see a mouth? Does the grasshopper have lips? Try to feed the grasshopper a leaf to watch the mouth parts move. Try to describe the mouth parts and how they move.

ANTENNAE Where are the antennae? Are they each a long, string-like, single appendage, or are they made up of many parts? Can you count the parts? Do they all look alike in size, shape and color? Why do you think a grasshopper needs the antennae? For what? Think about radio and television antennae.

MOTION We usually think that grasshoppers "hop." Do they also walk? How do they walk on the ground or floor? If possible, watch the grasshopper climb a small stick, weed stem, or blade of grass. Does it use all of its legs? Without hurting your grasshopper, place it on the ground and make it jump. (If it is an adult with wings, it may fly instead!) Follow it and make it hop or jump several times (at least five times). Does it hop the same distance each time? Measure or estimate the distance of each hop of flight. Does the grasshopper seem to get tired? What makes you think so?

NOISE Do grasshoppers make noises? If your grasshopper makes a noise, try to learn if it does it with its mouth or with some other part of its body.

COLORS Look at the whole grasshopper carefully. Is it the same color all over? Are the colors, shapes and sizes the same on both sides? What is attractive about your grasshopper? Is it clean? Watch to see what the grasshopper does to clean or groom itself.

HABITAT Where does the grasshopper live? What does it eat? Do grasshoppers live in your neighborhood year-round? Suggest two reasons that grasshoppers might not be seen where winters are cold (freezing temperature, not enough food).

CONCLUSIONS Did you think there were so many interesting things about a grasshopper? Do you think other insects might be as interesting? What other insects or small animals might be interesting to look at and learn more about?

about how difficult it is for a grasshopper to live very long in a captive state. How much space does a grasshopper need to live? Can you supply that in captivity? Tell the students that by studying grasshoppers, they have done what some scientists do. They have studied something very carefully to learn more about it. People have power over other animals in many circumstances. The students exercised power over the grasshoppers while they studied them. With that power comes important responsibility. In this case, the students exercised their power by making an effort to be careful in handling the grasshoppers and releasing them safely. Ask the students about other situations in which they feel a responsibility for their actions affecting animals. Examples: Taking care of pets, not leaving litter outside that can hurt wild animals. (See "Litter We Know.")

EXTENSIONS

1. Find out what contributions grasshoppers make to ecological systems. What animals use grasshoppers as a food source?
2. Some farmers and gardeners consider grasshoppers a nuisance. Find out why. Find out what actions, if any, are taken to reduce crop damage from grasshoppers in your region. Do the actions seem appropriate? Why or why not? See "Deadly Links" for a related activity about pesticides in the environment.

AQUATIC EXTENSION

Do this activity with a water-related insect, if possible. Adjust the specific questions as needed to suit the insect's characteristics, still using these general categories: Interesting Features, Legs, Wings, Head, Mouth, Antennae, Motion, Noise, Colors, Habitat, Conclusions.

EVALUATION

1. If you were a biologist studying wildlife, which of these could you study and call it wildlife: tigers in India, deer in the forest, cows on a farm, foxes in Iowa, sparrows in the city, spiders in the forest, ants in a building, rats in a garbage dump, white mice in a laboratory cage? (Probably all except the cows in a farm and the white mice in a laboratory cage.)
2. Name three wild animals that are smaller than a grasshopper.
3. Name three wild animals that are larger than a grasshopper.
4. Name three types of wildlife that have one of the same colors as your grasshoppers but aren't insects.
5. Create a simulation that shows how grasshoppers protect themselves from predators. This could be done in a kinesthetic activity format. In the simulation show how a grasshopper's body is adapted for survival.
6. Create several guidelines that people should follow when studying wildlife. Explain why those rules are important. When, if ever, is it acceptable for people studying wildlife to damage or kill wildlife?

from the **Project WILD Activity Guide**, produced by the Western Regional Enviornmental Education Council, Houston, Texas, second edition, 1992

44

Duplication

THIS is a good game for getting children interested in rocks, plants, and animals. Before assembling the children to play, secretly gather from the immediate area about 10 common natural objects, such as rocks, seeds, conifer cones, plant parts, and some signs of animal activity. Lay the objects out on a handkerchief and cover them with another handkerchief. Call the children close around you and tell them, *"Under this cloth are 10 natural objects that you'll be able to find nearby. I will lift the handkerchief for 25 seconds so you can take a good look and try to remember everything you see."*

After looking at the objects, the children spread out and collect identical items, keeping their findings to themselves. After five minutes of searching, call them back. Dramatically pull out the objects from under the handkerchief, one at a time, telling interesting stories about each one. As each object is presented, ask the children if they found one just like it.

Children have a lively curiosity about the kinds of things you'll show them—rocks, seeds, plants, and so on. When you repeat the game several times, it has a noticeable strengthening effect on the child's concentration and memory.

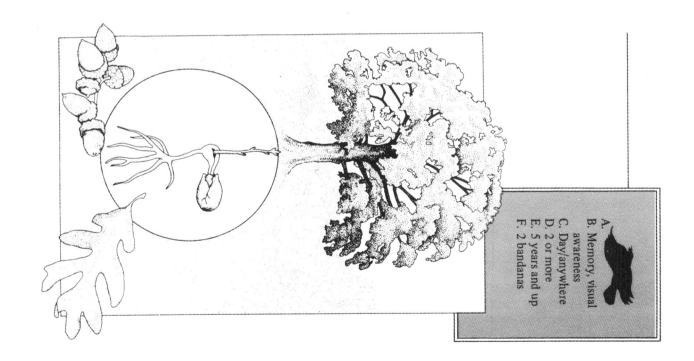

A.
B. Memory, visual awareness
C. Day/anywhere
D. 2 or more
E. 5 years and up
F. 2 bandanas

From **<u>Sharing Nature with Children</u>** by Joseph Cornell, DAWN Publications, Nevada City, CA, 1979

THE DRUMMING of a woodpecker. Wind rushing and roaring through the tree tops. The flute-like call of a hermit thrush. The "buzz" from a nearby hummingbird. Water cascading and singing down a steep, rocky incline.

A thrilling chorus of natural sounds delights the players in the Sound Map Game. Children love this activity—they become completely absorbed and sit surprisingly still while making their sound maps.

To play, begin by showing the group a 4 × 6 index card with an X in the center. Tell the players the card is a map, and that the X shows where they're sitting. When they hear a sound, they should make a mark on the card that aptly describes the sound. The mark's location should indicate as accurately as possible the direction and distance of the sound. The marks should be interpretive, not literal: the players don't have to draw pictures of plants and animals, just a few lines that represent the sound—for example, two wavy lines indicating wind, or a musical note indicating a songbird. In other words, they should spend little time drawing and most of the time listening.

Tell the players to keep their eyes closed while they listen. Explain that cupping their hands behind their ears provides a reflective surface for catching sounds, creating a shape like the sensitive ears of a fox or kangaroo. To hear sounds behind them, they needn't turn their heads, but just cup their hands in front of their ears.

Select a site where the group is likely to hear a variety of sounds—meadows, streams, and forests are fine. It's important to have everyone find a special "listening place" quickly, so that some aren't walking around while others are already listening. I usually give the group one minute to find a spot and tell them to stay in the same spot until the end of the game. Giving the players enough time to disperse fairly widely will ensure a diversity of sound maps and greater interest in sharing.

How long you should play depends on the group's age, attention span, and how well-supplied the environment is with sounds. A good basic guideline is 10 minutes for adults, 5–10 minutes for children. I like to call the group back together by imitating a natural sound or

blowing a crow or duck call. As the players assemble, ask them to share their maps with a partner.

It's sometimes hard to find a site that's protected from the sounds of cars and machinery, but these noisy areas are ideal for teaching lessons about noise pollution. Have the children make two sound maps, the first one near a busy street and the second in a quiet, natural spot. After the game, ask them where they felt more comfortable. This is a fine way to build children's conscious appreciation of natural areas.

After the children have drawn their maps and shared them, you can ask questions such as:

■ How many different sounds did you hear?
■ Which sounds did you like best?
■ Which sounds did you like least?
■ Which sounds had you never heard before? Why?
■ Which sounds had you never heard before? Do you know what made the sounds?

Instead of having them answer aloud, you can ask them to circle the sounds they'd never heard before, draw one line under sounds they liked best and two lines under the sounds they liked least.

Sound Map

A. Auditory awareness, calmness
B. Day and night/natural area
C. 1 or more
D. 5 years and up
E. Index card and pencil per player

From **Sharing the Joy of Nature** by Joseph Cornell, DAWN Publications, Nevada City, CA, 1989

Animal Tracks

Many animals are active at night. Others that are active in the daytime are shy and hide when people are around. To learn about animal activities, hunters and naturalists through the ages have learned to read the signs that animals left behind. These include tracks, droppings, feeding places, nests, and burrows.

The most informative of these, in terms of animal activities, are usually tracks. In identifying tracks, the shape of the paw, the presence or absence of nails on the paw, the size of the print, the comparison of front and hind prints, the distance between front and hind prints and between one set of prints and the next are all important. Frequently, tracks are not perfect, and even perfect tracks lose their detail as time passes. But if a combination of characteristics is used, even children can identify many animals by their tracks.

Cats and foxes both walk in a straight line and put their hind feet in their front footprints, but size of track, presence of nail prints in fox tracks, and area will usually make distinguishing one from the other easy.

Dogs make a pattern similar to cats but their hind feet seldom squarely hit the front track. The great American naturalist Dr. E. L. Palmer used to say dogs had lived around people too long and had gotten sloppy.

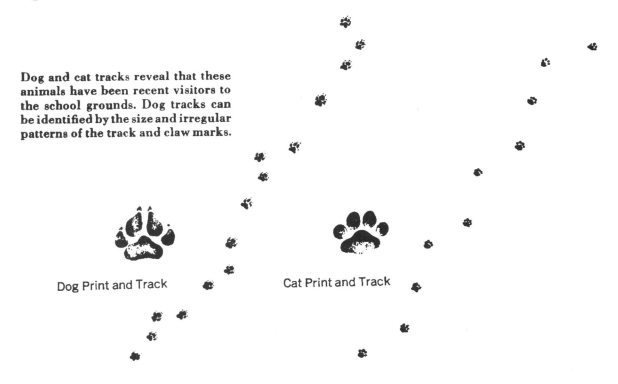

Dog and cat tracks reveal that these animals have been recent visitors to the school grounds. Dog tracks can be identified by the size and irregular patterns of the track and claw marks.

Dog Print and Track   Cat Print and Track

From **Ten Minute Field Trips: A Teacher's Guide to Using the Schoolgrounds for Environmental Studies** by Helen Ross Russell. Natonal Science Teachers Association, Washington, D.C., second edition, 1991

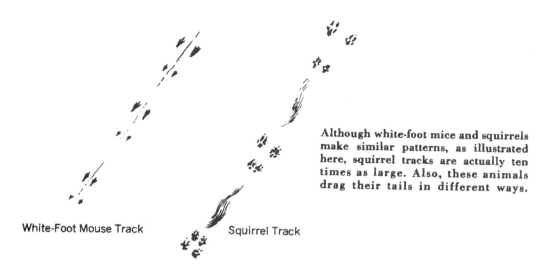

Although white-foot mice and squirrels make similar patterns, as illustrated here, squirrel tracks are actually ten times as large. Also, these animals drag their tails in different ways.

White-Foot Mouse Track   Squirrel Track

Squirrels and white-foot mice both hop by putting their small front feet down beside each other and swinging their larger hind feet in front of them. However, no one would confuse the size of a squirrel print with a mouse print.

Rabbits and field mice put one forefoot in front of the other, then swing their hind feet forward. Often when snow conditions are right, mice leave a tail print.

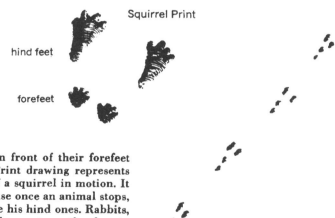

Squirrel Print

hind feet

forefeet

Animals swing their hind feet in front of their forefeet when they hop. The Squirrel Print drawing represents one set of tracks from a series of a squirrel in motion. It could never be a single set because once an animal stops, his forefoot marks would precede his hind ones. Rabbits, field mice, and other land dwellers put one forefoot in front of the other in hopping. Squirrels, deer mice and other tree dwellers put their forefeet down together.

Rabbit Track

Identification of the animal is only one part of the animal track story. More important is finding answers to questions like: "Where was the animal going?", "What was he doing?", "Did he travel across open space or around edges?", and "Did he find food?" Sometimes a drama involving several animals can be discovered, and excitement runs high.

Children love to feel they have a kinship with hunters of old, detectives, or Indians; but tracking is more than just fun. It is a good way to learn careful observation, to begin to understand the interrelatedness of all animal and plant life, to amass evidence, and to draw some conclusions.

RELATED CLASSROOM ACTIVITIES

Since a tracking trip frequently depends on two highly unpredictable things, the weather and animal behavior, a class may be prepared and then have to wait a long time. Or the trip can be a surprise to the children, with the only classroom preparation an invitation to go outside and learn, "what the squirrel did early this morning," or "how we can read animal tracks." After the trip, the stories read from fresh tracks may be written in essays or told in oral reports.

Children can make potato prints of the animal tracks. This is done by slicing a potato in half and drawing the track on the cut surface, then cutting out the track drawing from the rest of the potato. (Care, of course, must be taken when using knives, and children should always cut away from themselves.) The print thus made can be pressed on an inked stamp pad. A total track pattern like the grouped front and hind feet of a squirrel may be cut on one potato or the print of one foot like a dog or cat paw print can be made. Potato prints can be used to record the animal tracks which were observed or the children can compose new stories using the same animals or adding others. Using the potato prints, one group can illustrate a story for another group to interpret. Large murals on newspaper or brown paper may tell many animal stories, since many things occur simultaneously in nature. Children can begin to see the relationship between the size of the track and the size of the animal, the distance between tracks, and the direction of toe prints. Other easily cut materials such as cardboard or large erasers may be used instead of potatoes.

If plaster of Paris molds of animal tracks have been made outdoors, exact duplicates of the tracks can be made indoors by completely covering the mold with a coat of Vaseline or other greasy substance, putting a cardboard collar around it, and pouring plaster of Paris over it.

potato

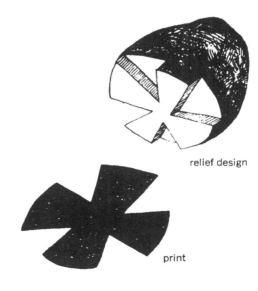

relief design

print

Potato Print

Making prints of animal tracks is an activity which can be done any time of year. Potatoes and other root crops can be used for these prints.

Animal Tracks

TEACHER PREPARATION

Alertness and flexibility are the best preparation for the study of animal tracks. In most school situations, tracks are not available just any time.

Furthermore, tracks do not last. Snow melts, more snow falls, or it rains. In areas of high population density (and most school grounds are), tracks get buried under other tracks. So preparing for an animal track lesson usually involves waiting, watching, and grabbing the opportunity.

FIELD TRIP POSSIBILITIES

1. Go outside in a light snow. Have a small child and a larger one go around the corner of the school building (so they are not seen by the class), walk across the snow, and return. Let the class identify the tracks of each. Have two children go around the corner of the building and instruct one to run and the other to walk. Can the children tell which tracks represent speed? What else can they learn from observing their own tracks?

2. Follow a squirrel's tracks in the snow. Where did the squirrel come from? Where did it go? Did it return to its starting point? Can you draw any conclusions? (Does it have more than one winter home? Is it still out hunting? Might it have gone home overhead?)

3. Look for bird tracks along a fence, in a weed patch, and along bushes. What conclusions can you draw about the size of the bird? Its method of traveling on the ground? Can you find a relationship between tracks and food? Tracks and shelter? Can you find tail and wing marks where birds landed?

4. Take a census of the number of dogs that crossed an area by the size of their prints. If several dogs were in the area, were they there at the same time or different times? Did they pay any attention to each other?

5. After a snow, do a study of people tracks on a sidewalk. Can you tell size, age, speed, direction of travel, or activity?

6. Go outside after a light snowfall and let the children use their hands and feet to make common animal tracks. Walk like a dog, cat, starling, pigeon, and squirrel; hop like a squirrel, rabbit, and sparrow.

7. Using plaster of Paris, cast a track. For outdoor use, put one inch of water in the bottom of a container; then add two inches of snow. Stir. Pour plaster of Paris so it makes a peak that extends an inch above the water. Stir. This mixture should be like whipped cream. If it isn't, add more plaster. Put a cardboard collar around the track. Pour the plaster so it gently flows into the print. Let it harden (this will take an hour or more).

8. Discover track stories in mud or fine dust.

9. If there are enough tracks of one animal to compare distance between sets of prints, can you draw any conclusions about speed of travel? Can you discover any reasons for the animal to be moving slowly? Quickly?

10. Can you find a track story that involves two different animals?

Acknowledgements

Ten New Hampshire schools participated in a 1992-93 pilot program. They field-tested the materials and the process outlined in these pages, and offered critical evaluative comments. Our thanks to those schools — and their teachers, students, and administrators — for their efforts and continued suppport of habitat enhancement projects.

Pilot program participants:

Allen Elementary School, Rochester
    Linda Day

Andover Elementary School, Andover
    Richard Birmele, Gail Hill, Ann Jones, Anne Marie Parr

Deerfield Community School, Deerfield
    James Arcari, Brenda Eaves, Matthew Ferguson, Bruce Turnquist

Kimball School, Concord
    Linda Becker, Kathi Mitchell, Jane Welch

McClelland Elementary School, Rochester
    Amanda Marrone, Anne Milne, Meghan Milne, Sharon Reed-Erickson

Milan Village School, Milan
    Christine Lindsey, Virginia Mondor, Lisa Morse

Milford Elementary School, Milford
    Chantal Alcox, Nancy Bannon, Silvia Belisle, Bill Carr,
    Jean French, Sue Heaton, Sarah Holder, Gloria Schooley

North Hampton Elementary School, North Hampton
    Jeanne Beland, Pat Cushing, Jim Clifford, Hope Miller,
    Pam Hopkins, Sue Reynolds, Linda Sherouse, Brenda Tharp

Ossipee Central School, Center Ossipee
    Sarah Barnes, Rachel Ward

Piermont Village School, Piermont
    Eileen Belyea, Sally Collete, Nancy Sandell, Lynne Spooner

White Mountain Regional High School
Vocational Special Education (S.T.E.P.), Whitefield
    Paul Ouimet

Permissions:
To produce this guide, we drew on a wealth of existing published material on the subject of habitat enhancement. We gratefully acknowledge the following authors, publishers, and organizations for extending permission to reprint their materials:

Dr. Lowell W. Adams, National Institute for Urban Wildlife

The American Forest Council, Project Learning Tree

Thomas G. Barnes, University of Kentucky Cooperative Extension

Janine M. Benyus

James L. Byford, University of Tennessee

Canadian Wildlife Federation

David J. Decker, Cornell University

Catherine A. Elliott, University of Maine Cooperative Extension

Ruth Shaw Ernst

Florida Game and Fresh Water Fish Commission

Fulcrum Publishing

Carrol Henderson, Minnesota Department of Natural Resources

Illinois Department of Conservation

Indiana Department of Natural Resources, Division of Forestry

David Langley, University of New Hampshire Cooperative Extension

Jenepher R. Lingelbach, Vermont Institute of Natural Science

Massachusetts Audubon Society

National Science Teacher's Association

National Wildlife Federation Oklahoma Conservation Commission

Oklahoma Department of Wildlife Conservation

Prentice Hall Press, A Division of Simon ~ Schuster

Project WILD, Western Regional Environmental Education Council

Jerry Schierloh, NewJersey School of Conservation,

Montclair State College

Randall Shank

David Sobel, Antioch/New England Graduate School

Teacher's Laboratory, Inc.

University of Connecticut Cooperative Extension

USDA Forest Service, Northeast Forest Experiment Station

Utah Department of Natural Resources

Virginia Wildlife Magazine, Virginia Game Department

Washington Department of Wildlife

Draft Reviewers:

Thank you to all who reviewed this guide, for their invaluable critical commentary:

Sarah Barnes, Ossipee Central School

Linda Becker, Kimball School

Bill Carr, Milford Elementary School

Miriam Dunne, New Jersey Department of
    Environmental Protection & Energy

Ellie Horwitz, Massachusetts Division of Fisheries and Wildlife

Lisa Kane, Maine Department of Fish and Wildlife

John Kanter, University of New Hampshire Cooperative Extension

David Langley, University of New Hampshire Cooperative Extension

Marion Larson, Massachusetts Division of Fisheries and Wildlife

Kathi Mitchell, Kimball School

Paul Ouimet, White Mountain Regional High School

Jerry Schierloh, New Jersey School of Conservation

Jeffrey S. Wallner, Environmental Interpreter

Rachel Ward, Ossipee Central School

Jane Welch, Kimball School

Dennis Yockers, Wisconsin Department of Public Instruction